# STUDIES IN RENAISSANCE SCIENCE

# *Toward Modern Science*
## II
*Volume*

**EDITED BY ROBERT M. PALTER**

*The Noonday Press*
*a subsidiary of*
*Farrar, Straus & Cudahy*          *New York*

# CONTENTS

Volume **I**

*Volume* II


# Renaissance Science

# The Transition to Modern Science

# Renaissance Science

*George Sarton*

# THE QUEST FOR TRUTH:
# A BRIEF ACCOUNT OF SCIENTIFIC
# PROGRESS DURING THE
# RENAISSANCE*[1]

As this lecture is delivered to a general audience, I may be permitted to preface it with a few remarks on the history of science. Many people misunderstand science, and hence one can hardly expect them to have a fair idea of its history. The history of science might be defined as the history of the discovery of objective truth, of the gradual conquest of matter by the human mind; it describes the age-long and endless struggle for the freedom of thought—its freedom from violence, intolerance, error, and superstition.

The history of science is one of the essential parts of the spiritual history of mankind; the other main parts are the history of art and the history of religion. It differs from these other parts in that the development of knowledge is the only development which is truly cumulative and progressive. Hence, if we try to explain the progress

* Reprinted from *The Renaissance: A Symposium* (New York, 1953), pp. 35-49, with the permission of the Metropolitan Museum of Art.
[1] Many years ago, I took part in another symposium on the Renaissance organized by Mount Holyoke College. My contribution, "Science in the Renaissance," was included in *The Civilization of the Renaissance,* by James Westfall Thompson and others (University of Chicago Press, 1929). I have never reread it; hence this lecture is independent of it.

of mankind, the history of science should be the very axis of our explanation.

Another preliminary remark is needed to define the frame of this study. It is not enough to say "the Renaissance," because that word is not understood by everybody in the same way. Let us define it as the period which elapsed between the Middle Ages and the modern age, but the Middle Ages did not end abruptly and the modern age did not begin suddenly, and their ends and beginnings were not by any means the same in different countries. Italy was ahead of the other countries and her awakening was already begun by the middle of the fourteenth century, in Petrarch's time. We might define the Renaissance *grosso modo* as the period extending from about 1350 to the death of Giordano Bruno in 1600, or to the death of Cervantes and Shakespeare in 1616; one might even stretch it a little further, to 1632, when Galileo published his first great book, the *Dialogo dei due massimi sistemi del mondo*.[2] Remember that every great book of science closes a period and opens a new one. Remember also that no period is valid for all nations nor for the whole of any single nation, for the men and women living at any one time are never spiritual contemporaries. Some of our own contemporaries have not even reached the Renaissance— they are still living in the Middle Ages; others are not even as advanced as that; they are still living in the Stone Age. It is because of such disparities that the progress of technology is so frightening; our ancestors were uneasy when guns were used by children; our own fears are deeper, and we shudder to think that atomic bombs might fall into the hands of men who, in every respect (except technology) are still barbarians.

To return to the Renaissance, it was, among other things, a revolt against medieval concepts and methods. Of course, every generation reacts against the preceding one; every period is a revolt against the preceding one, and so on. Yet, in this case, the revolt

[2] That *Dialogo* is, to a large extent, an epitome of Renaissance thought. It will be easier to appreciate this when the new English text, edited and elucidated by Giorgio de Santillana, is published by the University of Chicago. It is scheduled to appear in 1952. [Published in 1953.—Ed.]

was a bit sharper than it usually is. It is not sufficiently realized that the Renaissance was not simply a revolt against scholasticism; it was also directed against Arabic influences (especially those represented by Avicenna and Averroës). The anti-Arabic drive was in full swing in Petrarch's time. Such a revolt and struggle for independence was a symptom of growing strength. In spite of its triumph it was not completed; there are still many Arabic elements in our language and in our culture.

One of the medieval traits was the fear of novelties.[3] The Renaissance was more tolerant of them and sometimes it welcomed them, or went out of its way in order to find more of them. Each novelty created trouble, but as they impinged on the minds with increasing frequency, one got used to them and distrusted them less; one ended by liking them. In most cases, however, the novelties were rather superficial. For example, the Renaissance artists discovered the beauty of the human body, but that had never been completely forgotten.[4] They discovered the beauties of ancient art, new accents in poetry, new rhythms in music; they discovered ancient books and were anxious to publish them. All that was very exhilarating.

In the field of science, the novelties were gigantic, revolutionary. This explains why timid people are afraid of science; their instinct is sound enough; nothing can be more revolutionary than the growth of knowledge; science is at the root of every social change. The Renaissance scientists introduced not a "new look" but a new being. The novelty was often so great that one could hardly speak of a Renaissance or rebirth; it was a real birth, a new beginning.

Put it this way: The Renaissance was a transmutation of values, a "new deal," a reshuffling of cards, but most of the cards were old; the scientific Renaissance was a "new deal," but many of the cards were new. This will be shown simply and briefly, too briefly. I cannot help that. My message must be delivered in a single lecture. It is as if I were invited to paint as quickly as possible an immense

---

[3] That fear was reflected in the language; for example, the Arabic word *bidca* means novelty, but it also means heresy. The Spanish word *novedad* had similar undertones.

[4] For medieval examples, see my *Introd.* (3, 1256).

fresco. Here it is. The fresco will be divided into a dozen panels, which I shall invite you to contemplate, with indulgence, one after another.

## I. THE DISCOVERY OF THE EARTH

Geographical discoveries were initiated by Henry the Navigator, and in this respect the Renaissance was heralded not by Italians but by Portuguese. Their initiative was followed gradually by other nations. It is hardly necessary to recite those heroic deeds, for everybody is familiar with them. A few names will suffice to awaken your memories: Bartholomeu Dias (1488), Columbus (1492), Vasco da Gama (1498), Amerigo Vespucci (1497-1504), Magellan (1519-22), etc. The Renaissance was truly the golden age of geographical discovery; by the year 1600 the surface of the known earth was doubled. Was not that an achievement of incredible pregnancy? The earth was doubled! It was not only a matter of quantity, but one of quality as well. New climates, new aspects of nature were revealed.

Ancient and medieval navigations had been largely coastal; mariners seldom spent many days without sight of land. They knew the seas, but now they had conquered the oceans; they learned to know the arctic regions, the deserts and the tropics.

Each of us can measure those novelties, for if he searches his own mind, he may be able to recapture the deep emotions which he felt when he found himself for the first time in the middle of the ocean, or in the heart of a tropical jungle, or when he tried to cross a desert or glacier. These discoveries, which are fundamental for each of us individually, were made for the whole of mankind in the fifteenth and sixteenth centuries.

We are all aware of those geographical discoveries which added new continents and innumerable islands to our estates, but relatively few people realize that new aspects of nature were discovered in the very heart of Europe, that is, the high Alps, which earlier men had been afraid of exploring. This was a new world in the heart of the old one. The severity and danger of the Alpine climate had deluded medieval minds into believing that the high mountains were the abode of gnomes and devils. In this they were less advanced than the Buddhists of India, China, and Japan, who regarded the mountains as sacred, and built temples on their slopes and at the very tops. The earliest Alpine expeditions began very timidly in the fourteenth century, but did not assume any importance before the sixteenth century; by the end of that century some forty-seven summits had been reached.[5] Two main purposes could be served in Alpine expeditions; the first was aesthetic or religious, the second was scientific. One might risk one's life in difficult ascents in order to enjoy the beauty of nature and the sublimity of God, or in order to understand the mysterious climate obtaining at high altitudes, and to observe the shape of the mountains and the plants and animals that inhabited them. The first man to combine in himself both purposes was Leonardo da Vinci.

## II. THE NEW EDUCATION

Any renaissance must express itself in the field of education, for when men begin to think and feel in a new way they are eager to modify teaching methods in proportion to their own spiritual change. Unfortunately, the great majority of schools were informal and the teacher of genius could hardly emerge from the local and temporal circumstances which limited his activities. For example, the *Casa giocosa* established by Vittorino da Feltre in Mantua in 1423 did not survive him. The same remark might be made about great educators like the Catalan Juan Luis Vives (1492-1540) and

5 The first treatise *ad hoc* was that of Josias Simler: *De Alpibus* (Zürich, 1574). It is a very curious fact that Alpinism stopped at the end of the sixteenth century and did not begin again in earnest until the end of the eighteenth century.

the Englishman Roger Ascham (1515-68). New pedagogical ideas cannot be effective unless they be incorporated in an educational system of some permanence.

A development of greater stability had been begun in the meantime by the Brothers of the Common Life in the Netherlands, at the very end of the fourteenth century. By the way, this is another aspect of the early Renaissance which is not Italian. Its importance can hardly be exaggerated. The *Devotio moderna* was an attempt to reconcile the humanities with Christianity. This could be done only on a mystical plane, but the Dutch Brothers did it very well, and their influence spread rapidly in northwestern Europe. By the middle of the fifteenth century there were already some 150 of their schools in the Netherlands, France, and Germany, and those schools remained the best of their kind until the sixteenth century. Many great men were educated by the Brothers of the Common Life, the two most famous ones being Cardinal Nicholas of Cusa (1401-64), who loved them, and Erasmus of Rotterdam (1466-1536), who was irritated by them. By Erasmus' time the schools had lost their spiritual power; in the second half of the sixteenth century they were replaced and eclipsed by the Jesuit colleges.

Much credit for the educational revival must be given also to the reformers. From the Protestant point of view, a modicum of education was a religious duty. Every Christian should be able to read the Scriptures by himself. Therefore, Martin Luther was very deeply concerned with public education. In 1524, Magdeburg organized new schools on the plan which he had recommended. Other schools were established in many German cities, and their availability to the children was gradually increased; it has been claimed that the public school system of the German Protestant states was the first model of our own. The inspirer and organizer of that system was Philip Melanchton (1497-1560), whose influence was so pervading and lasting that he fully deserved the title given to him, *Praeceptor Germaniae.*

### III. THE NEW MATHEMATICS

Historians of art never fail to discuss the new conception of perspective which was largely due to Florentine artists but which grew
also in Flanders and Germany. This implied a certain amount of
mathematical thinking, but that amount was very small, almost
negligible. The new mathematics which we have in mind is something more profound and infinitely more complex. We cannot do
more than refer to its main aspects, and the references are almost
meaningless except for mathematical students, but this cannot be
helped. The history of mathematical ideas is peculiarly difficult to
explain (even to mathematicians), because the first achievements
were made in Babylonia, matured in Greece, incubated in the
Arabic world, and gradually reappeared in the West. The astonishing flowering of the fifteenth and sixteenth centuries concerned
trigonometry and algebra. Trigonometry was revived by Germans
like Regiomontanus (1436-76), then by Georgius Rhaeticus and
Bartholomaeus Pitiscus; algebra by Italians, like Scipione del Ferro,
Nicola Tartaglia, Geronimo Cardano (1501-76), and Lodovico
Ferrari. The gradual introduction of a number of operational sym-
bols prepared the writing of equations as we do, and the theory of
equations began to take shape. The climax of Renaissance mathematics was reached by such men as the Italian Raffaele Bombelli
(fl. 1572), the Frenchman François Viète (1540-1603), and the
Fleming Simon Stevin (1548-1620). In 1585, the last named published his invention of decimal fractions and decimal weights and
measures. He then explained with great lucidity an idea which the
Anglo-Saxon world has not yet been able to grasp to this day.

These mathematical discoveries were not as tangible as the geographical ones; yet they were deeper. The Conquistadores were
very materialistic, greedy and inhuman; the mathematicians were
the opposite in every respect and their conquests were spiritual
ones, conquests of pure reason, the scope of which was infinite.

## IV. THE NEW ASTRONOMY

Now let us travel to Frombork in Poland, where Copernicus was ending his days in 1543. His great treatise, the first copy of which was brought to him on his deathbed, explained the new astronomy. It was not radically new, for the fundamental idea of it had been outlined before by Aristarchos of Samos during another Renaissance (the Hellenistic Renaissance of Alexandria). Yet, Aristarchos' views had been rejected by the leading astronomers of antiquity and had been driven underground. To re-explain them, as Copernicus did after more than eighteen centuries of discredit, was very much the same as a new creation. The sun was put back in the center of the world, and the earth reduced to a planetary status. The implications of this as set forth by Giordano Bruno and others were not simply of astronomical interest, but of philosophical importance. It is a strange paradox that at the very time when man was beginning to conquer nature, he was obliged to drive himself away from the center of things; in proportion as he grew wiser he had to make himself smaller. That is all right, of course. The purpose of science is to discover the truth irrespective of consequences.

It is pleasant to recall that Copernicus was helped in his computations by a much younger man, Georg Joachim Rhaeticus, who visited him and lived with him for more than two years. In 1539, when Rhaeticus arrived, he was only 25, while Copernicus was 66. The main point is this: Copernicus was a canon of the Cathedral of Frombork, while Rhaeticus was a professor in the Protestant University of Wittenberg. At a time when the hatred dividing Catholics from Protestants was getting as hot as hell-fire, the old canon and the young Protestant mathematician were living and working together like brothers. Science is not simply international, it is almost always *au dessus de la mëlée;* it unites all men in a sublime task, the quest for truth. It may be added that in the sixteenth century Catholic and Protestant theologians were united in one common hatred, their hatred of the Copernican theory, which conflicted with the Scriptures.

Copernicus was a poor observer and it had been easier for him (as it had been for Aristarchos) to formulate his new theory, because he was not embarrassed by good observations. (Science proceeds by successive approximations; if the early astronomers had been given excellent telescopes, they would have been so bewildered that they would have been unable to understand anything.) The new vision which had been opened by Copernicus warmed the enthusiasm of a Danish boy, Tycho Brahe, who was to become one of the best astronomical observers of all time. He was able to accumulate a large mass of observations which were more accurate than his simple instruments seemed to warrant, but these observations increased his perplexities, and he felt obliged to abandon the heliocentric hypothesis (even as Hipparchos had felt obliged to do seventeen centuries before him) and to adopt a kind of compromise. This was not the first time (nor the last) that careful observations drove out a theory which was good, but not good enough, and required some corrections in order to be admissible. The final establishment of the Copernican theory by Johann Kepler (1609, 1619) is outside our frame, yet the fact remains that Copernicus was the first to formulate it without equivocation. This he did in 1543.

Many medieval astronomers had realized the growing inadequacy of the Julian calendar, but their claims for reform had remained unheeded. Pope Gregory XIII, helped by the Bavarian mathematician, Christopher Clavius, and buoyed up by the spirit of novelty which informed his time, finally accomplished the much needed reform. The "novelty" was less profound than that of the Copernican theory, but it was more tangible to the mass of the people. The good Catholics who went to sleep on October 4, 1582, woke up the next morning on October 15. That was startling enough, was it not? But the surprise was restricted to Catholics. The reform had come just too late; if it had been decided upon before the Reformation, the whole of Latin Christendom would have accepted it without demur. At this time, however, self-respecting Protestants could not receive a new calendar from the hands of their chief adversary. Therefore, they continued to use the Julian calendar (in England until as late as 1752), and one could already have taunted them with Voltaire's sarcasm: Those idiots "prefer to disagree with the sun than to agree with the Pope."

## V. THE NEW PHYSICS AND CHEMISTRY

Changes in physics were less radical than in other fields, and the situation of chemistry was even more confused. The medieval incubation of mechanical ideas was not by any means completed. We owe many little clarifications to Italians like Tartaglia, Cardano, Benedetti, Guido Ubaldo; but the ablest clarifier before Galileo was the Fleming, Simon Stevin. Stevin, the greatest mechanician in the nineteen centuries between Archimedes and Galileo, introduced new ideas into statics and into hydrostatics.

In the meantime, the intense rivalries of colonizing nations encouraged the progress of navigation and of the physical sciences which would increase the accuracy of sailings and minimize their dangers. The main requirements were geodetic, astronomic (better methods of taking the ship's bearings), cartographic; one needed faster ships and better instruments to navigate them. Geodetic improvements were due to the Frenchman Jean Fernel and the Dutchman Gemma Frisius; better maps to the Portuguese Pedro Nuñez and the Flemings Gerhard Mercator and Abraham Ortelius. Who has not seen the splendid geographic atlases which were produced in the sixteenth century? Not only did they provide a large mass of information of vital importance to statesmen and merchants; some of their maps were so beautiful that it is a joy to look at them.

One of the first fruits of oceanic navigation was a better knowledge of magnetic declination, for the compass was one of the sailor's best instruments, but its readings could not be trusted without taking occasional deviations into account. The magnetic observations and other knowledge useful for navigation were put together by Englishmen like Robert Norman (1581) and William Barlow (1597) and by Simon Stevin (1599). At the very end of the Renaissance, William Gilbert published the first great treatise on magnetism (1600); it is significant that his knowledge of terrestrial magnetism, rudimentary as it still was, induced him to outline cosmological implications.

In optics the best work was done by Italians like Giovanni Battista della Porta (1538?-1615) and Maurolycus, but progress was not very tangible. In spite of the fact that so few physical (and chemical) phenomena could be accounted for in rational terms, the results were so alluring that the investigators were full of conceit. They were aware of the nearness of mysteries the penetration of which might expose them to suspicion. Della Porta's famous book was entitled *Magia naturalis* (1538). Various little academies were founded in Italy during the sixteenth century; they were somewhat in the nature of exclusive clubs and secret societies; the members were often known to each other by nicknames; their academies offered them means of discussing the elusive "secrets" which they hoped and feared to disclose. At any rate, they gave them privacy and protection against the misunderstandings of the ignorant and the bigots.

Physical "secrets" included chemical ones, but in the field of chemistry the fundamental ideas were even more difficult to separate and to define. Vision and understanding were obscured by alchemical fancies around which had gathered all kinds of superstitions. The defeat of alchemy was not really begun until the end of the seventeenth century, and its completion required still another century of patient work. In the Renaissance it was out of the question, and historians of chemistry look upon that period as the golden age of alchemy.

## VI. THE NEW TECHNOLOGY

The only branch of technology which has never become inactive is the art of warfare. In this age, as in all others, most technicians were concerned with that art, trying to find new weapons, to improve the old ones, or to defend themselves more effectively against the weapons of their enemies. The invention of new arms and new armor was always the main obsession of men, good or bad.[6] Even as great an artist and as serene a man as Leonardo da Vinci was obliged to devote much of his attention to such problems. Yet the greatest invention of the Renaissance was a peaceful one: the invention of typography. It is hardly necessary to indicate what the art of printing meant for the diffusion of culture, but one should not lay too much stress on diffusion and should speak more of standardization. Every manuscript was in many respects unique. Printing made it possible for the first time to publish hundreds of copies that were alike and yet might be scattered everywhere. It was now possible (as it had never been before) to refer to a definite statement made on page X of such or such a book; the reference made by a scholar in Oxford might be checked immediately by his colleagues in Salamanca, in Bruges, or in Vienna. Steady advance implies the exact determination of every previous step; this now became incomparably easier. That "divine art," as the early typographers did not hesitate to call it, was invented about the middle of the fifteenth century in Germany. Thus, we see once more that the early Renaissance was not exclusively Italian; the most pregnant initiatives were taken far away from Italy—in Portugal, in Holland, and in Germany.

The invention of typography was considerably enriched by the invention of engraving, which was accomplished and vulgarized at about the same time. Woodcuts and copperplates did for the

---

[6] A list of early treatises on war technology is given in my *Introd.* (3, 1550-54). Those technicians were Germans or Italians.

graphic arts exactly what printing did for letters. Works of art could be diffused and standardized. The two inventions, printing and engraving, were of immense importance for the development of knowledge. Printing made possible the publication of mathematical and astronomical tables which could be depended upon; engraving, the publication of books with illustrations representing plants, animals, anatomical or surgical details, chemical apparatus, etc. One good figure is more revealing than many pages of text; the use of illustrations obliged the author to be more precise than he could have been, or wished to be, without them.

The new technology was symbolized by the publication of illustrated treatises by Vannoccio Biringuccio of Siena (1540), Georgius Agricola (1556), Lazarus Ercker (1574), all of which included a wealth of information on mining, metallurgy, chemistry, the founding of guns and bells, the making of weapons and gunpowder, the casting of alloys such as type metal, the coining of money, and many other arts and crafts. This suggests that, thanks to printing and engraving, the Renaissance was a vigorous age of stocktaking and encyclopaedism as well as of invention. Every bit of knowledge could now be garnered and preserved forever. Words and images were immortalized.

## VII. THE NEW BOTANY

One aspect of the Renaissance has often been described and emphasized: the publication of the Latin and Greek classics, many of which had been lost because they were represented by single manuscripts, which were buried and forgotten in the corners of neglected libraries. The discovery of such manuscripts was as thrilling as the discovery today of papyri or clay tablets. There were incunabula editions of the great botanical books of antiquity, those of Theophrastus and Dioscorides, but those early editions were not illustrated. The descriptions of plants, even when correct, were confusing, because they referred to another flora than that of western Europe. In this case, the classics had to be rejected and the work of botanical description had to be done over. The pioneers, "the fathers of botany," were Germans like Otto Brunfels (1530), Leonhard Fuchs (1542), Hieronymus Bock, and Valerius Cordus; and they were followed by Flemings like Dodonaeus, Clusius, Lobelius, Busbecq, by Englishmen, Italians, etc. Not only were new herbals illustrated, some of the illustrations were very beautiful.

Botany was then an essential part of medical teaching, and the use of illustrated herbals intensified the need of direct observations. The ancient botanists had been satisfied mostly with names, an abundance of synonyms, and the enumeration of qualities or virtues; the German "fathers" and their followers had added images; now there was a growing desire to see and handle the plants themselves. Botanical gardens were attached to the medical schools (the first university garden was in Padua, 1545); dried plants were collected in herbaria by Luca Ghini (who died in Bologna in 1556) and by many others. A new botanical knowledge was within reach, and brisk emulation caused it to grow rapidly in a great many places.

## VIII. THE NEW ZOOLOGY (AND MINERALOGY)

Animals were studied in the same spirit as plants, and students of natural history were stimulated by the discovery of new countries beyond the seas, where plants and animals were either radically new, or sufficiently different from those already known, to be startling, to cause perplexities, and to invite further investigations. There emerged a new kind of scientist, the traveling naturalist, the scientific explorer. The greedy adventurers of early days were now replaced by men in search of knowledge. The quest for truth inspired them with a missionary zeal, and they were prepared to suffer many hardships for the sake of science.

The discoveries made in foreign lands excited the naturalists who were obliged to stay at home, such as physicians, professors, and the keepers of botanical gardens and greenhouses, and necessitated their describing more accurately and more completely the faunas and floras of their own countries. Thus exploration abroad caused deeper investigations and led to better knowledge of all the forms of life which could be observed nearer home.

This reminds me that I almost forgot to speak of the mineralogical investigations. Some minerals were generally included in the early herbals, and the search for mineral drugs was increased in the sixteenth century. The main mineralogical work, however, was done and had always been done by prospectors in search of rich ores. This was part of the business of mining, such as was described in *De re metallica* of Agricola (1556), mentioned above. The collectors of precious stones had never stopped their activities, and their business was roused when more gold and silver was mined in Europe and America.

By 1600 the knowledge of the three kingdoms of nature was radically different from what it had been in the Middle Ages; it was incomparably richer, and, what matters even more, it was more genuine; a larger proportion of it was based on direct observations. This does not mean, unfortunately, that all the early fantasies had been eliminated; the average Renaissance naturalist was able to make good observations, and he became abler to make better ones every year, but few of them were strong enough to reject deeply-rooted superstitions. The amount of information, old and new, genuine or not, was so enormous by the second half of the sixteenth century that it made necessary the encyclopaedic efforts of Conrad Gesner of Zürich and of Ulisse Aldrovandi of Bologna.

IX. THE NEW ANATOMY

The new anatomy was created by Leonardo da Vinci and by Andreas Vesalius of Brussels. Leonardo was not an amateur anatomist, as so many artists were, but an indefatigable investigator who spent more time in elaborate dissections than most professionals. He examined almost every organ of the human body, taking copious notes and making admirable drawings; yet all that work was kept in his archives and remained practically unknown until the last century. On the other hand, Vesalius published in 1543 his *Fabrica,* which became known at once and which marks the beginning of a new era in anatomical studies. Mark that the same year, 1543, was the era of the new anatomy as well as of the new astronomy; it was one of the golden years of the Renaissance.

## X. THE NEW MEDICINE

Among many great physicians it must suffice in this brief outline to mention three who were outstanding in their respective lines, true pioneers who represent three different countries: the Swiss Paracelsus, the Italian Girolamo Fracastoro, and the Frenchman Ambroise Paré.

Paracelsus of Einsiedeln, near Zürich, is the best exemplar of the new medicine which had not yet completely emerged from medieval confusion. At his best, he was a pioneer in many directions—in the study of mental diseases, as the founder of iatrochemistry (chemistry applied to medicine), and as the distant herald of homeopathy. He was an adventurous experimentalist, yet his sounder views were crudely mixed with metaphysical and magical ideas, and his rational cures could not always be separated from miraculous ones. His study of the diseases of miners was the first to be devoted to occupational or industrial medicine. He was original to the point of extravagance, indiscreet and bombastic, generous and foolish—a kind of medical gypsy, restless and dogmatic, a man of genius, a great doctor, and a charlatan.

The scientific fame of Fracastoro of Verona rests mainly on his treatise on contagion (1546), in which he suggested that infection is caused by the transmission, from a person who is diseased to one who is healthy, of minute bodies capable of self-multiplication. This was an adumbration of modern theories (it could not be more before the discovery of microscopes and much else). His popular fame was based on another book of his to which we shall refer presently.

Ambroise Paré (1510-90) was a military surgeon whose native genius had not been inhibited by the scholastic medical education of his time and by irrelevant Latin learning; he was able, therefore, to take full advantage of every one of his innumerable observations with an open mind. He introduced so many novelties that he may be called the founder of modern surgery. His modesty was equal to his experience; it is well illustrated by a familiar statement of his: *"Je le pansai, Dieu le guerit"* (I dressed his wound, God healed it).

These three great men reveal the complexity of the Renaissance, for they were as different as they could be: Paracelsus the rebel, Fracastoro the classicist, Paré the wise practitioner. Paracelsus' genius was still in many respects medieval, Fracastoro's ancient, Paré's modern; yet they were children of the same century.

## XI. NEW DISEASES

It was not enough for the Renaissance to have great physicians; the age indulged itself in new diseases. When we said above that one might consider the middle of the fourteenth century as its starting point, we were not thinking only of Petrarch and Boccaccio and of the new culture which they symbolized, but also of the Black Death, whose first outburst (in 1348-52) was so terrible that one-fourth of the population was destroyed and another fourth at least completely demoralized. This was perhaps the most frightful calamity of its kind in history, and it was of such extent and rigor that one could hardly find a better dividing line between the old age (the Middle Ages) and the new one. The Black Death did not stop in 1352; it flared up repeatedly throughout the fourteenth century and later. It was not, however, even in 1348, a new disease, but simply the worst example of a very old one.

The Renaissance suffered two other diseases which were peculiarly its own. The first, physical, was syphilis; the second, mental, was the fear of witchcraft.

Syphilis made so dramatic an appearance at the siege of Naples in 1495 that it is difficult to resist the conclusion that it was really a new disease imported from the new world. That hypothesis cannot be completely proved,[7] but it is strengthened by two sets of considerations. In the first place, syphilis has very definite symptoms, and it is hard to believe that all of the great physicians of the past would have overlooked them if they had been present. There is no mention of those symptoms and no description of any disease suggesting syphilis in the abundant medical writings anterior to 1495, in Greek, Arabic, or Latin. In the second place, the explosive development of syphilis at the end of the fifteenth century suggests that it was a new disease for which Europeans were utterly unprepared.[8] The lack of syphilis literature before 1495 was compensated by its abundance afterwards.

The most remarkable publication *ad hoc* was the Latin poem written by Fracastoro in 1531, if only because it was that poem which gave its name to that disease (after the romantic shepherd Syphilus, who contracted it).[9] Fracastoro's poem enjoyed considerable popularity. The author's main intention was to sing the praise of a new remedy *guaiacan* (*guaiacum, lignum sanctum,* holy wood). The discovery of that wonderful drug (as it was thought to be at the beginning) confirms the American origin of the disease. According to a medieval conceit, God had placed remedies close to the diseases which they could cure, counter-poisons near the

[7] The literature concerning the origin of syphilis is immense and never ceases to grow. As Editor of *Isis,* I receive every year a few more books or papers on the subject.

[8] In the same way, smallpox, introduced by Europeans into America, destroyed a very large number of Indians (*Isis* 37, 124). Many other examples could be adduced concerning not only human diseases, but also plant and animal pests.

[9] Syphilis is the only disease having a poetic name.

poisons, etc. Now, if syphilis came from the West Indies, it was natural to hunt for a drug in that part of the world. This was done and the herb duly found; it was the one which the Indians called in their language *guaiacan*.

The German humanist Ulrich von Hutten (1488-1523), who had cured himself with *guaiacan* wrote a treatise on the subject (1519) which he dedicated to the Archbishop of Mainz. At the end of it he did not scruple to say something like this: "I hope that Your Eminence has escaped the pox, but should you catch it (Heaven forbid, but one can never tell) I would be glad to treat and cure you." This is another typical Renaissance trait. The good archbishop realized that no offense was meant and took none. Syphilis was then a terrible disease (more terrible than now), but it was not considered more disgraceful than other diseases, and it caused less hypocrisy than it does today.

The other disease, much more terrible than syphilis, was the fear of witchcraft which became virulent at about the same time. The virulence was caused by a bull of Innocent VIII (1484) and exacerbated by the *Malleus maleficarum* (1486). This was a treatise written for the guidance of inquisitors; it explained how to detect, convict, and punish the witches. Looking at it from our point of view it might be considered a textbook of sexual psychopathology. The fear of witches caused their persecution, and the persecutions increased the fears. There appeared and spread everywhere a mass psychosis the like of which was not experienced again until our own days. The procedure followed in many witch trials was scrupulously recorded, and therefore we are very well informed. Many witches confessed their crimes and described their association with the Devil; their descriptions of the latter tally so often that one might take them as an objective proof of his reality. These poor women who were burned to death were neurotics whom we would send to hospitals. The witchcraft delusion could not be cured by theologians, who could detect only sin and heresy; it was instead a matter for physicians who recognized pathological conditions. The first physician to see that was the Dutchman Johann Weyer, who cannot be praised too highly for doing what he did as early as 1563.[10]

These medical subjects have been discussed at greater length than the others, because they are easy to describe and because they illustrate some aspects of the Renaissance less glorious than the usual ones, yet essential for its understanding. The sixteenth century was a golden age of humanities and of art, but it was also an age of intolerance[11] and cruelty; it proved itself sometimes to be inhuman to a degree which was hardly surpassed at any time except our own.

## XII. THE NEW ARTS

To return to more pleasant aspects (we must recognize the gloomy parts, though it is unwise to dwell on them overmuch), the quest for truth was so continuous and fervent and it was carried on by so many great men of many nations that mankind approached much closer to its goal, and at greater speed, than had been possible in medieval times. The consequences of that quest can be observed in every kind of endeavor, whether material or spiritual.

Speaking in this Museum, it is natural to choose as our example the field of art. Take perspective. That was in a sense a mathematical subject, but its adaptation to drawing and painting was realized in the fifteenth century by a number of artists: Filippo Brunelleschi, Leon Battista Alberti, Paolo Uccello, Piero della Francesca, Leonardo da Vinci (all of them Tuscan or closely connected with Florence). The first two were architects, and it is hardly necessary to point out the many connections between architecture, on the one

[10] For more information on this very great man see *Isis* 25, 147-52, 1936.
[11] I have not spoken of the wars between Catholics and Protestants which disgraced Europe and Christendom, because that would have taken me too far aside. The repressions of witchcraft and heresy were often confused by the inquisitors, and more so by the public. We should be indulgent, because similar delusions and confessions disgrace our own times. All considered, it is not quite as disgraceful, however, to kill one another in the name of Marx as to do so in the name of Christ.

hand, and mathematics, physics, and engineering, on the other. The architectural renaissance implied a scientific renaissance. The painters needed not only the new geometrical (or linear) perspective; they needed also the subtler knowledge to which the Middle Ages had given the same ambiguous name, perspective—aerial perspective, we call it. This was a mixture of optics, meteorology, and theory of shades and colors. With regard to this, artists received some assistance from men of science, but the best work in the West was done by Leonardo da Vinci. In their fresh enthusiasm for the beauty of human forms the artists needed some knowledge of anatomy, and here again Leonardo was their outstanding guide. Other tasks required the help of geographers, geologists, mineralogists, naturalists, and in this case the best exemplar (aside from Leonardo) was the Frenchman Bernard Palissy.

The main problems of life cannot be solved by men of science alone, nor by artists and humanists. We need the coöperation of all of them. Science is always necessary, never sufficient; we are starving for beauty, and where charity is lacking, nothing else is of any avail.

To return to art and science, the need of both and the feeling for both, the most illustrious representatives of that ambivalence are the Florentine, Leonardo da Vinci (1452-1519), and Albrecht Dürer (1471-1528) of Nuremberg. They were contemporaries, the second a little younger than the first; but they did not meet, nor did they influence each other to any degree. Being children of the same eld, their scientific problems were the same, but Dürer devoted more time to art, and Leonardo to science. Leonardo was a better scientist and a deeper philosopher than Dürer. He was, above all, a great anatomist and a great technician; he invented many machines, but (this is almost incredible) he paid no attention to the greatest inventions of his age (indeed, of all ages), printing and engraving. On the other hand, Dürer, being a practical man, a man of business, was one of the first to exploit both inventions. He created hundreds of woodcuts and engravings, and three books were written, illustrated, engraved, printed, and published by him. Leonardo was a dreamer and, from the world's point of view, a failure; Dürer was a very successful man. I can admire them both, but I love Leonardo. He was the finest flower of the Renaissance, the best illustration of that radiant age in two respects: the first is the one indicated by the very name Renaissance—rebirth, novelty (everybody appreciates that); the second is the realization, more complete in himself than in any other man, that art and science, the pursuit of beauty and the pursuit of truth, are two complementary undertakings.

Leonardo saw clearly five hundred years ago what very few people are able to see today, and the few who do see it can only do so because they are standing on his shoulders.

It would have pleased me very much to speak much more of Leonardo, but I was obliged to restrain myself for two reasons: the first is that if I had let myself go, I could hardly have spoken of anybody else; and the second is that I know Professor Panofsky is going to deal with him in the last lecture, and I do not wish to steal his thunder.

A final remark. Rapid and oversimplified as it has been, my account has brought to light, among other things, the fact that the quest for knowledge has always been international or supranational, even more fundamentally so than the quest for beauty. The Italians could have created all of their masterpieces just as well if the Germans, the Flemings, and the English had not existed. On the contrary, scientific discoveries always implied the collaboration of many nations. No scientific achievement can ever be explained within the limits of a single country. This was made clear in my summary, in spite of the fact that it was necessarily restricted to the western world. If I had been able to speak of India, China, and Japan, I would have shown many curious relationships, but my time has been too short to do justice to the West alone, and hence I had to abandon the East. Please remember that and forgive me.

The personality of Leonardo was so overwhelming that it embraced many Oriental elements as well as western ones. This is another title of his to our admiration and our gratitude.

*Dana B. Durand*

# TRADITION AND INNOVATION IN FIFTEENTH CENTURY ITALY[*][1]

## "IL PRIMATO DELL' ITALIA" IN THE FIELD OF SCIENCE

The immediate purpose of this symposium, I take it, is to weigh the elements of tradition against those of innovation in fifteenth-century Italian science and scientific thought. The ultimate purpose is to test in a single instance the validity of the opinion, commonly held since Burckhardt, that the Quattrocento marks a radical break with the Middle Ages and institutes the era of Modern Europe. The instance is crucial, since by general consent science is fundamental to the modern world, and yet Burckhardt in his *Culture of the Renaissance in Italy* ignored it almost completely.

What I shall examine may be described in the phrase "il primato dell' Italia," the primacy claimed for Italy in the field of science, more narrowly in the fields of scientific methodology, cosmology, mathematics and physics. In order to simplify the discussion, I have confined myself largely to the speculative aspects of these disciplines, leaving aside the fruitful work of artists and craftsmen who

[*] Reprinted from *Journal of the History of Ideas,* IV, 1 (January, 1943), 1-20, with the permission of the *Journal of the History of Ideas.*
[1] This paper, together with the critique by Dr. Baron, was delivered at the Renaissance session of the American Historical Association meeting at Chicago, December 29, 1941. At the kind invitation of Dr. Randall, it was submitted to the *Journal of the History of Ideas* as the basis of a symposium on fifteenth-century Italian science. In order not to diminish the force of Dr. Baron's critique, it was decided to publish the paper substantially as given at Chicago, confining revision chiefly to matters of detail.

bridged the gap between the theoretical and the productive or practical activities. The happy union of the hand, the eye, and the mind, which reached its perfection in Leonardo da Vinci, was undeniably a chief glory of Quattrocento Italy, and contributed significantly to the sixteenth-century scientific tradition leading up to Galileo. But the task of assessing the relative importance of the operational and the theoretical contributions to the whole of Quattrocento science must wait for further monographic research.[2]

Without attempting to set up a rigorous theory of historical process, I should like to indicate the methodological considerations which have governed the preparation of this paper. I make use of organic analogies without insisting upon them, since the application of biological categories to the study of intellectual history can hardly be carried out with full consistency.

In general, by tradition one may understand the persistence of a germ plasm, a tissue of forms, categories and habits of speculative thought, in this case the medieval structure of Christian dogma, the scholastic method, the Aristotelian-Ptolemaic cosmos, peripatetic metaphysic and science, etc. Tradition also includes the highly diversified operational skills, developed and accumulated over centuries by craftsmen, artists and other technical and manual workers; but these, as I have stated, will not be treated in the present paper.

Innovation would seem to result from two types of cause, the first being internal elaboration of purely traditional substance. The

---

[2] The fundamental work on this subject is Leonardo Olschki, *Geschichte der neusprachlichen wissenschaftlichen Literatur:* I, *Die Literatur der Technik und der angewandten Wissenschaften vom Mittelalter bis zur Renaissance* (Heidelberg, 1919); II, *Bildung und Wissenschaft im Zeitalter der Renaissance in Italien* (Leipzig, 1922); III, *Galilei und seine Zeit* (Halle a. S., 1927). Cf. also the numerous studies of Edgar Zilsel, which are particularly illuminating for the sixteenth- and seventeenth-century phases of the relation between craftsmen and men of science, especially "The Sociological Roots of Science," *American Journal of Sociology,* XLVII (1942), 544-562. The obverse of the "mechanic" scientist is the aristocratic "virtuoso"; cf. Walter E. Houghton, Jr., "The English Virtuoso in the Seventeenth Century," *Journal of the History of Ideas,* III (1942), 51-73, 190-219.— In general for the subjects treated in this symposium the most useful bibliography is that prepared by F. R. Johnson and S. V. Larkey in *Modern Language Quarterly,* II (1941), 363-401.

scholastic method, so frequently dismissed as sterile, was in fact peculiarly apt to produce this type of innovation. Its typical instrument, the *questio* form of commentary, by the very fact that it began with a statement—however perfunctory—of the arguments *against* an accepted or orthodox position was bound in certain minds to provoke an interest in the arguments *for* the radical or heterodox position. And in time this speculative interest was likely to ripen into veiled and even overt conviction. This phenomenon, this skeptical and even perverse turning away from established notions, was often the outcome of sheer ennui with the stereotyped arguments of the schools.[3] Masking itself with irony as a protection against ecclesiastical condemnation, this skepticism flourished in fourteenth-century Paris and Oxford, and persisted in the fifteenth century at Padua and the other Italian universities. In my opinion the critical elaboration of scholastic tradition—particularly in the commentaries on Aristotle—forms the most important component of Quattrocento philosophy and science.

The other chief source of change may be described as full intellectual mutation. This type of change may be purely spontaneous, as in the unanalyzable creative intuition of an individual of genius. It may result from cross-fertilization, an influx of foreign scholars and teachers, or from fresh blood in the form of rediscovered texts and new translations. Finally, mutational change may result from social, political, or economic crises of the type which were so frequent in the lively history of the Italian cities and states. Thus Dr. Baron's studies of Quattrocento humanism and the ideal of civic virtue have shown that fundamental alterations were introduced into the concept of citizenship by Florentine reaction to the threat of Viscontean hegemony.[4]

[3] On the heterodox tendencies of fourteeth-century speculative thought, see the various studies of Konstantin Michalski, especially "La physique nouvelle et les différents courants philosophiques au xiv^e siècle," *Bulletin international de l'Académie Polonaise des Sciences et des Lettres,* classe de philologie, classe d'histoire et de philosophie (1927), 158-164.

[4] Of Dr. Baron's numerous studies on Florentine political humanism, see especially "A Sociological Interpretation of the Early Renaissance in Florence," *South Atlantic Quarterly,* XXXVIII (1939), 427-448.

As an illustration of the interplay of these forces of tradition and innovation, I should like to discuss briefly the special case of cartography, a minor branch of science which has usually reflected quite faithfully the developments taking place in the major branches.[5] In the field of cartography a definite primacy has been claimed for fifteenth- and sixteenth-century Italy, and especially for Florence.[6] Although my own monographic study in fifteenth-century German cartography has suggested certain restrictions to the Italian claim, it has not led me to question the reality of the Italian "primato." The nature of this primacy proves, however, to be very complex. It may be broken down roughly into the following elements: 1) a strong persistence of traditional material, including, a) the stereotyped wheel-map of the so-called T-O form, going back through the Middle and Dark Ages to the *Orbis Terrarum* of Agrippa, and beyond that to the primitive map-frame of the Ionians, b) rudimentary mathematical and astronomical geography embedded in scholastic science, particularly the elements of spherical trigonometry and map projection derived from Ptolemy's *Almagest,* and tables of terrestrial latitudes and longitudes appended to the Latin translations of Arabic astronomical works, c) empirical surveys dating back to the thirteenth and early fourteenth centuries, including both the astonishingly accurate marine charts known as *portolani,* and cruder topographic and hydrographic surveys which had been combined with data from written itineraries to form rudimentary land maps. 2) These traditional elements were trans-

[5] This discussion of cartography is based largely on my monograph *The Vienna-Klosterneuburg Map Corpus of the Fifteenth Century,* 2 vols. (Leiden: E. J. Brill, 1940?) [Publication of the work appears to have been interrupted in May 1940. A copy of the corrected proof has been deposited in the Harvard College Library where it can be consulted by those who are interested.]

[6] On Florentine "primacy," see Roberto Almagià, "Il primato di Firenze negli studi geografici durante i secoli XV e XVI," *Atti della Società Italiana per il Progresso delle Scienze,* XVIII Riunione, (1929), I, 60-80. The priority claimed for the Florentines in creating the *Tabulae Modernae* of Italy, Spain, France, and possibly other regions, has been contested by Father Joseph Fischer, S.J., in his monumental *Claudii Ptolemaei Geographiae . . . Commentatio* (Lugduni Batavorum, Lipsiae, 1932). In any case, the ultimate origin of these maps remains obscure.

formed in the fifteenth century by a) internal modification and elaboration in the scholastic universities, in the humanistic coteries, and in the professional scriptoria and printing houses, combining all of the traditional elements mentioned above with the newly discovered maps of Ptolemy; b) mutational changes, of which the translation of Ptolemy's *Geographia* by Jacopo d'Angelo in 1406 was by far the most important. The fact that this capital text had been overlooked by the medieval translators may be regarded as one of the momentous accidents of history; its recovery as one of the most notable successes of early scientific humanism. Mutational innovations appear to have been inspired, though not actually produced, by two individuals of genius, the Florentine Toscanelli and the non-Italian Nicholas of Cusa.[7] The progress of cartography was also furthered by a number of critical events in the political and ecclesiastical sphere, of which three may be mentioned: i) the extension of Venetian power on *terra firma* in the first half of the fifteenth century; one consequence of this policy was the practice of making regional and topographic surveys for fiscal and military purposes, which were used for the construction of panoramas and maps. ii) The Council of Florence in 1439 provided a unique opportunity for the meeting of scholars from all parts of Europe, and

[7] Extravagant claims have been made for Toscanelli as a geographer by G. Uzielli, *La vita e i tempi di Paolo dal Pozzo Toscanelli* (Rome, 1894), *passim*. Cf. the devastating critique of Uzielli by H. Wagner, "Die Rekonstruktion der Toscanelli-Karte . . . ," *Nachrichten von der K. Gesellschaft der Wissenschaften zu Göttingen,* phil.-hist. Kl., (1894), 208-312. The precise nature of the famous map which Toscanelli is supposed to have sent to Columbus is still obscure. There is good ground, however, for believing that Toscanelli, at the Council of Florence, was the central figure in a cosmopolitan group of scholars who were interested in compiling modernized maps to supplement the *Geographia* of Ptolemy; cf. J. Fischer, S.J., *Die zur Cusanus-Karte gehörige Descriptio Germaniae Modernae* (Prague, 1936). Father Fischer's conjecture is supported by an interesting discovery of Aubrey Diller, "A Geographical Treatise by Georgius Gemistus Pletho," *Isis,* XXVII (1937), 441-451. The treatise in question is an extension of Strabo; Diller's note raises the question, about which little is known, of the role of Strabo in Renaissance geography. The Latin translation made by Guarino, appears to have been widely known in humanistic circles, but its influence on scientific geography, unlike that of Ptolemy, cannot be described as mutational.

informal discussion of geographical questions was a natural by-product of such a cosmopolitan gathering. The original inspiration of the so-called Nicholas of Cusa Map, formerly thought to be the first modern map of Central Europe, appears to date from this occasion. iii) A second ecclesiastical event, the great Papal Jubilee in 1450, also brought together a group of non-Italian cartographers, this time in the house of Cardinal Nicholas of Cusa in Rome. The actual drafting of the Cusa Map appears to date from the following year, but there can be no doubt that it represents the end stage of a process which had been going on for nearly a generation. This process, the modernization of Ptolemy, was complex, tentative and obscure. Nevertheless it can be analyzed in sufficient detail to show that the unit of creative innovation at any given point is small, the persistence of tradition great. The rôle of non-Italians, especially Germans and Scandinavians, is in some respects decisive in the primacy of Florentine cartography during the Quattrocento.

I have ventured to discuss the case of cartography in some detail, because it furnishes a sort of paradigm which may be applied to other sciences of broader scope. In the four branches of exact science which I propose to treat in this paper, monographic research has not yet proceeded very far; many of the general statements which I shall be obliged to make in so condensed a discussion may, therefore, prove to be incorrect in the light of future research. The way has been prepared, however, by the work of two great scholars, Pierre Duhem[8] and Lynn Thorndike,[9] and with their guidance we shall not go far astray. It is, indeed, only fair to point out that both these men are animated to some extent by a bias against fifteenth-century Italy, which has led them to minimize its scientific achieve-

[8] Pierre Duhem, *Études sur Léonard de Vinci*, 3 series (Paris, 1906-1913); *Le système du monde*, 5 vols. (Paris, 1913-1917) [five more volumes have recently been published; see Bibliography.—Ed.]. So far as I am aware, there is still no satisfactory critical study of Duhem's achievement as an historian of science.

[9] Thorndike, *A History of Magic and Experimental Science*, 6 vols. (New York, 1923-1941). For a critical discussion of Thorndike's monumental achievement, see my article "Magic and Experimental Science; the Achievement of Lynn Thorndike," *Isis*, XXXIII (1942), 691-712.

ment. Duhem, a devout Catholic and a patriotic Frenchman, sought to depreciate the achievement of Galileo—and thereby indirectly to vindicate the condemnation imposed by the Church on the great Florentine—by showing that it came as the end stage of a long tradition of speculative science, originating in the schools of fourteenth-century Paris. Thorndike, on the other hand, seems to have been animated by a certain personal antipathy toward the Renaissance. He has systematically run down the scientific achievements of the more famous fifteenth- and sixteenth-century figures, especially when they had been over-praised by contemporary humanists and by modern historians.

The broad findings of Thorndike and Duhem have not been effectively challenged, but criticism of detail has seriously restricted some of the latter's sweeping interpretations. The outlines of a new and subtler concept of Italian "primato" are beginning to take shape, a concept in which scholasticism and humanism, Middle Ages and Renaissance, cisalpine and transalpine learning, tradition and innovation assume interdependent instead of opposing rôles.

The most impressive example of this re-interpretation of Italian primacy in the field of science is to be found in the recent article of J. H. Randall, Jr., entitled "The Development of Scientific Method in the School of Padua." [10] Of course the claim of Italian "primato" in this field was nothing new. Raffaello Caverni, at the close of the nineteenth century, spun out the history of the "metodo sperimentale" in Italy through six rambling and not very reliable volumes.[11] Caverni asserted varying degrees of Italian pre-eminence or priority in experimental science throughout the period since the thirteenth century. Like Duhem, he minimized the absolute originality of Galileo, but, on the other hand, he attributed considerable creative importance to the Quattrocento.

The superiority of Randall's brilliant study over most of its predecessors lies in the fact that it has no axe to grind—a merit which

[10] Randall's article appeared in the *Journal of the History of Ideas,* I (1940), 177-206.
[11] Caverni, *Storia del metodo sperimentale in Italia,* 6 vols. (Florence, 1891-1898).

American scholarship is often able to display. Randall has shown that over a period of more than three centuries (from Pietro d'Abano at the beginning of the fourteenth to Cremonini at the beginning of the seventeenth century) the physicians, the logicians and the physicists of Padua devoted their energies to the perfection of the technique and methodology of scientific investigation. The originality of the Paduan method lay in its combination of the *compositive* and the *resolutive* approach, advancing from effects to causes and regressing from causes to effects. Randall's demonstration of the continuity of this Paduan tradition should kill once and for all the myth that Francis Bacon and René Descartes pulled scientific method out of the hat, like a rabbit. The only question which might be raised is whether this dual method, this combination of "induction" and "deduction," originated and developed exclusively at Padua, or whether it did not undergo a parallel development in the northern schools. Randall's account clearly implies the elaboration of traditional material, especially of Aristotle and Galen. Mutational elements were introduced by the cross-fertilization of disciplines, specifically of medicine and physics[12]—which had been closely associated since the end of the twelfth century—with the elaborate logic of the later Middle Ages. A further cross-fertilization appears to have been introduced through the passage of Averroistic and nominalistic teachings from Paris to Padua.[13] During the Quattrocento no mutational advances appear to have taken

[12] The traditional alliance of medicine and physics, which goes back to the 12th century in western Europe, was represented in 15th-century Italy by such names as James of Forli, Giovanni Marliani, Ugo Benzi of Siena. The compatibility of scholasticism and humanism in Renaissance medicine is implied, in the case of Benzi, by the study of Dean P. Lockwood, "Prolegomena to the Life and Works of Ugo Benzi," *Transactions and Studies of the College of Physicians of Philadelphia*, 4th ser., vol. VIII (1940), 125-131.

[13] On Paduan Averroism, see Erminio Troilo, "L'Averroismo Padovano," *Società Italiana per il Progresso delle Scienze*, XXVI Riunione (Rome, 1938), vol. III, fasc. 2, pt. iv, and other articles by a number of scholars, *loc. cit.* The tendency of this group of studies is to emphasize the "modernity" of Paduan Averroism. Troilo has been scornfully attacked by the apologist of Italian humanism, Giuseppe Toffanin, in a letter published in *La Rinascità,* II (1939), 56-72. It is not easy for an outsider to ascertain the nature of the animus which lies beneath this controversy.

place, which can be associated with the translation or recovery of new material, or with the creative intuition of a man of outstanding genius. The decisive summations of this slowly evolving line of thought were not achieved until the close of the sixteenth century (Zabarella).

In the other branches of exact science which I shall examine, the threads of a continuous Italian tradition have not been spun together so compactly by modern historians. In the case of the first of these branches—cosmology and astronomy—the developments of the later Middle Ages and the Quattrocento have been interpreted primarily as background for Copernicus. Italian and German historians have sharply contested the primacy for their respective countries in the fifteenth century, and Duhem has claimed it for France in the fourteenth.[14] Germans have read anticipations of Copernicus into the mystico-scientific speculations of Nicholas of Cusa.[15] Italians have been disposed to accept this, and other in-

[14] On fourteenth-century French pre-eminence in the field of astronomy, see Duhem, *Système du monde,* vol. IV, *passim.* Five volumes of this great work, left in MS at the author's death, remain unpublished. Their publication, announced by the firm of A. Hermann, Paris, has presumably been interrupted by the war. Lacking these volumes which continue the history of cosmological theories to Copernicus, we are unable to determine the nature of Duhem's final judgment on fifteenth-century Italian astronomy. It may be inferred from his other writings, however, that this judgment was depreciatory. It is possible that Duhem's views may have been challenged by Ernst Zinner, who is reported to have published an important bibliography and study of Renaissance astronomy. Apparently no copy of this work has been received from Germany. [*Geschichte und bibliographie der astronomischen literatur in Deutschland zur zeit der renaissance,* Leipzig, K. W. Hiersemann, 1941.—Ed.]
[15] The magnification of Nicholas of Cusa as a precursor of Copernicus goes back to Giordano Bruno. It was given modern currency by F. J. Clemens, *Giordano Bruno und Nicolaus von Cusa* (Bonn, 1847), and it has been "debunked" with excessive severity by Thorndike, *Science and Thought in the Fifteenth Century* (New York, 1929), ch. VII. *Cf.* Ernst Hoffmann, *Cusanus Studien:* I, *Das Universum des Nikolaus von Cues,* Sitzungsberichte der Heidelberger Akademie der Wissenschaften, phil.-hist. Kl., XX (1930), No. 3. Hoffmann's scholarly study has a *Textbeilage* by Raymond Klibansky giving an accurate transcription of the Cardinal's famous astronomical note on which Clemens built his case for the Copernican anticipation. Other accounts of the Cusan cosmology, both more favorable than that of Thorndike, are to be found in E. Cassirer, *Individuum und Kosmos in der Philoso-*

stances of what might be called the "Cusanus-intrusion" into the Italian "primato," contenting themselves with insisting that the learned Cardinal derived his inspiration from contact with Italian scholars, particularly with Alberti and Toscanelli.[16] Moreover, in the case of cosmology, they assert that the decisive influence on Copernicus came, not from the Cusa tradition, but from the teachings of Domenico Maria Novara at Bologna.[17] In the field of empirical astronomy, Italians point with pride to Toscanelli's remarkable observations of Halley's comet in 1456.[18] Germans hail their Regiomontanus who also observed the movements of the comet, though in less detail, and who planned, though he did not live to carry out, the first series of systematic astronomical observations in modern times.[19]

---

phie der Renaissance (Leipzig and Berlin, 1927), ch. I, passim, and Dietrich Mahnke, Unendliche Sphäre und Allmittelpunkt (Halle a. S., 1937), 76-106.

[16] Italian writers have not only accepted but emphasized the originality of Nicholas of Cusa, particularly in the field of philosophy. This tradition of the "Cusanus-intrusion," which has been accepted by most neo-idealist writers, appears to have started with Francesco Fiorentino, Il Risorgimento filosofico nel Quattrocento (Naples, 1885).

[17] The Italian case for the influence of Novara on Copernicus is presented by Lino Sighinolfi, "Domenico Maria Novara e Nicolò Copernico," Studi e memorie per la storia dell' Università di Bologna, V (1920), 205-231. Sighinolfi suggests that the idea of the earth's motion may have been discussed by Novara and by certain fifteenth-century Italian humanists, but he gives no evidence to support this conjecture.

[18] Uzielli, op. cit., 481, states flatly that Toscanelli was the inspirer of both Cusa and Regiomontanus in the field of cartography, and elsewhere emphasizes his influence on the mathematical speculations of the learned Cardinal. Chapter VI, written by G. Celoria, describes and analyzes in detail the comet observations which Toscanelli noted between 1433 and 1472. Celoria speaks of Toscanelli as "la più gagliarda forza riformatrice del tempo suo" (378), claims that the observations of 1456, "rispetto al loro tempo sono e per la forma e per la sostanza assolutamente nuove ed originali" (344), and blames modern Italian writers for neglecting the memorials of their own astronomical achievement, thereby allowing northerners to claim credit of priority which, in the case of Regiomontanus, is not deserved (378 ff.).

[19] Regiomontanus has recently received his definitive biography at the hand of Ernst Zinner, Leben und Wirken des Johannes Müller von Königsberg, genannt Regiomontanus (Munich, 1938). Thorndike, Science and Thought, ch. VIII, attempted to deflate the reputations of both Regiomontanus and his master, George Peurbach. But Zinner's biography effectively counters Thorndike's attack. Regiomontanus, as Zinner shows, was obsessed with the idea of reforming the Ptolemaic cosmology. But whether he ever reached the point

Without attempting to decide in favor of either German or Italian chauvinism, the following restrictions may be applied to the claims of both: a) In astronomy and cosmology the persistence of tradition is very strong throughout the fifteenth century.[20] The basic astronomical material is still substantially that which was current in the Middle Ages, namely Ptolemy's *Almagest*, the standard Arabic tables and texts, the thirteenth-century *Alphonsine Tables* with modifications and revisions from fourteenth-century Paris and Oxford. b) No mutational elements of significance appear to have been introduced in the fifteenth century. There were no major translations or discoveries. The much vaunted revision of the *Almagest*, initiated by George Peurbach and completed by Regiomontanus, was little more than an epitome with few alterations of substance.[21] Both Toscanelli and Regiomontanus professed to be aware that the traditional Ptolemaic-Alphonsine astronomy stood in need of revision, but the observational data and the calculational theory at their disposal were insufficient for the task. It is true that Domenico Maria Novara, noting a discrepancy between Ptolemaic data and observations made in his own day, was led to suggest that terrestrial latitude had actually changed—a surmise which has received unexpected confirmation in our own day. He also attempted

---

of abandoning the geocentric theory is doubtful. He made a marginal note "Aristarchus Samius" opposite Archimedes' reference to the possibility that the earth might revolve about the sun (203). Zinner believes it probable that Copernicus, through Domenico Maria Novara, became acquainted with Regiomontanus' project of reforming the theory of planetary motions, a project which was frustrated by his premature death (204 f.).

[20] The extent to which fifteenth-century astronomical manuscripts reproduce earlier material is apparent from an examination of Zinner's *Verzeichnis der astronomischen Handschriften des deutschen Kulturgebietes* (Munich, 1925). A survey of Italian manuscripts, on the same scale, would yield similar results.

[21] Zinner, (*Regiomontanus*, 60-63), points out, as against Thorndike, that the *Epitome* incorporates material from Arabic astronomy and other sources. Nevertheless, Zinner's account leaves one with the unmistakable impression that the *Epitome* was far from a revolutionary work. It was still based on the translation of Gerard of Cremona, despite the availability of a recent translation by George of Trebizond. Although it served as the textbook of both Copernicus and Galileo, it could hardly have provided the inspiration for a new cosmological system.

a new determination of the inclination of the ecliptic; but similar attempts had been made in France two centuries earlier with results of comparable or superior accuracy.[22] What Copernicus may have learned from his sojourn at Bologna we have no way of knowing, since the scientific legacy of Domenico Maria, which was still extant in the seventeenth century, has disappeared.[23]

If the practical reformation of Ptolemy's astronomy was more in the nature of a wish than a fulfillment, the speculative critique of his cosmology could point to certain tangible achievements. These, however, as Duhem has shown, were chiefly the work of fourteenth-century Paris scholastics. The principal inroad into Ptolemaic-Aristotelian orthodoxy was the theory of the diurnal rotation of the earth.[24] This was a purely speculative cosmology, not founded on any actual observations. It kept the structure of the geocentric system, but inverted its dynamics, immobilizing the sphere of the fixed stars and releasing the earth for a daily spin on its own axis. The theory of the diurnal rotation first lifted its head in Paris about 1300. It was discussed in a multitude of *Questiones* throughout the fourteenth century, usually only to be rejected. The

[22] There were a number of independent observations of the inclination of the ecliptic, made by both Arabic and medieval European astronomers. Thus in 1289 Guillaume of St. Cloud, one of the most accurate observers in the West, (he gave the latitude of Paris as 48°50′, accurate to the minute) determined the inclination at 23°34′ (correct value at that time, 23°32.5′).

[23] On the loss of Novara's writings, cf. D. Berti, *Copernico e le vicende del sistema copernicano in Italia* (Rome, 1876), 44, 178. It is possible that a careful search of Italian libraries might result in the discovery of some of Novara's books.

[24] The importance of the theory of the diurnal rotation of the earth was first brought out by Duhem in connection with Nicole Oresme; "Un précurseur français de Copernic: Nicole Oresme (1377)," *Revue générale des sciences pures et appliquées,* XX (1909), 866-873. Oresme's commentary and French version of *De Caelo* (*Du Ciel et du monde*), in which the most radical defense of the theory is to be found, is being edited by A. J. Denomy and A. D. Menut; only Book I has appeared so far, *Medieval Studies,* III (1941), 185-280. A more conservative discussion appears in Buridan's Latin commentary on the *De Caelo,* which has been edited by Ernest A. Moody (to be published in the near future by the Medieval Academy of America). A useful *mise au point,* though by no means a conclusive treatment, is Grant McColley, "The Theory of the Diurnal Rotation of the Earth," *Isis,* XXVI (1937), 392-402.

first to espouse it openly was Nicole Oresme, the most imaginative
scientific thinker of the later schools, but, bold as he was, even
Oresme approached this novelty with coyness and circumspection.
There is no evidence that the theory of the diurnal rotation was
further elaborated in the fifteenth century by either Germans or
Italians. It appears to have been accepted, along with certain other
modifications of the Ptolemaic system, in a few Italian circles of the
early sixteenth century, but it is not clear whether, through them, it
influenced Copernicus.[25]

The other chief departure from Ptolemaic-Aristotelian orthodoxy was the doctrine of a plurality of worlds.[26] The notion that
God could have, and actually may have created other worlds outside our own—perhaps infinite in number and extent—was a play-
thing of the late medieval schools. Rejected by Aristotle, defended
by the Epicureans, the plurality of worlds, as Professor Lovejoy has
shown, was a logical consequence of the Platonic principle of plenitude. In the late thirteenth century both plenitude and plurality
had triumphed, at least officially, over the constitutional restrictions
that the peripatetic wing of scholasticism had sought to impose on
divine omnipotence. In the fourteenth century, as a result of ecclesiastical pronouncement, the notion of the plurality of worlds was
generally, although not universally, accepted. It was passed on to

25 We are not sufficiently informed on the cosmological views of the Italian
contemporaries of Copernicus to know whether they supported the theory
of the diurnal rotation. References to the motion of the earth may refer, as
in the case of Celio Calcagnini, to a slow rotation of the earth's axis about
the celestial poles, or to some sort of "trepidation" theory, such as had been
developed by the Arabs. McColley has recently shown that Giorgio Valla
in his *De Expetendis et Fugiendis Rebus Opus* advocated the so-called geo-
heliocentric theory, later associated with the name of Tycho Brahe (*Isis*,
XXXIII [1941], 312-314). McColley points out that no less than four systems of cosmology competed with the revised Ptolemaic during the sixteenth
and seventeenth centuries.
26 The importance of the "plurality of worlds" is again a discovery of Duhem
which has been followed up by McColley; "The Seventeenth Century Doctrine of a Plurality of Worlds," *Annals of Science*, I (1936), 385-430; see
also *Speculum*, XII (1937), 386-389 for an account of the same doctrine in
St. Bonaventura, Franciscus Mayronis and William Vorilong. On the connection between the plurality of worlds and the principle of plenitude, see
A. O. Lovejoy, *The Great Chain of Being* (Cambridge, Mass., 1936), ch. IV.

Quattrocento Italy, where it appears to have undergone no significant development. It is possible that Nicholas of Cusa introduced a mutational element through his semi-mystical exaltation of the earth as identical in nature with the "noble" stars. Leonardo da Vinci echoed the Cusan suggestion, and a century later, Giordano Bruno fused it into the Copernican cosmology, deriving from this fusion a new conception of an infinite universe. The origin of Bruno's enthusiastic vision must be traced back, not only to humanistic philosophers of the Quattrocento, but also to those subtle scholastics who had refused to hedge divinity with Aristotle's finite fence.

In mathematics, as in astronomy, the primacy of the fifteenth century has been disputed between Germans and Italians. In the purely utilitarian field of commercial arithmetic, Italy for two centuries had been supreme.[27] Manuscript and printed algorisms and *Rechenbücher* [28] circulated extensively in Central Europe after the middle of the fifteenth century, but these were usually nothing more than translations and adaptations of Italian models.[29] In less narrowly practical fields, in algebra and trigonometry, the pre-eminence of Italy was directly challenged by German schools, especially the University of Vienna. Regiomontanus is reported to have taken the Italian universities by storm, captivating academic audiences at Padua and Bologna by his humanistic eloquence and his

[27] Italian primacy in mathematics dates from Leonardo Fibonacci. The most important recent studies are those of Ettore Bortolotti, especially: "Il primato dell' Italia nel campo della matematica," *Atti della XXVII Riunione della Società Italiana per il Progresso delle Scienze* (Rome, 1939); "L'infinito ed il limite nel Rinascimento italiano," *Bollettino della Unione Matematica Italiana*, I (1939), 275-286.

[28] Perhaps the earliest German *Rechenbuch,* the *Algorismus Ratisponensis* (ca. 1445), appears to have been compiled by Frater Fridericus Amann of Regensburg, through whom the most important documents in the Vienna-Klosterneuburg map corpus have been transmitted (Durand, *op. cit.,* 76). This work, written in a curious hodge-podge of Latin and German, bears the evidence of derivation from an Italian model.

[29] The numerous commercial arithmetics of 15th-century Italy perhaps deserve a more thorough study than they have received. Dr. Allan Evans prepared an extensive list of MSS of these algorisms, in connection with his edition of Peglotti's *Practica della Mercatura* (Cambridge, Mass., 1936), but the list has not been published.

personal charm, quite as much as by his undeniable scientific virtuosity. Regiomontanus attempted to start a mathematical and astronomical correspondence with Giovanni Bianchini, "facile princeps" of contemporary Italian mathematicians.[30] Regiomontanus envisaged an exchange of problems and answers to be based on friendly emulation, but the older Italian was speedily scared away by the precocity of the enthusiastic German.

In the purely speculative field, the Quattrocento has sometimes been credited with the origins of modern mathematicism, that is the philosophical and scientific approach to the study of natural phenomena through precise quantitative measurement and specification. E. A. Burtt has attempted to show that mathematicism was born of Neo-Pythagorean metaphysics, developed by Nicholas of Cusa, and transmitted through Copernicus and the sixteenth-century Italian school to the age of Galileo, Kepler and Descartes.[31]

[30] The correspondence of Regiomontanus with Bianchini and other contemporary mathematicians was edited by Maximilian Curtze (Abhandlungen zur Geschichte der mathematischen Wissenschaften, XII, XIII, Leipzig, 1902). Cf. also S. Magrini, *Johannes de Blanchinis ferrariensis e il suo carteggio scientifico col Regiomontano (1463-4)*, Atti e Memorie della Deputazione Ferrarese di Storia Patria, vol. XXIII, (1917), fasc. 3. There is no satisfactory account of Bianchini's scientific work, either as astronomer or as mathematician. Zinner (*Regiomontanus,* 69-80) presents the Italian as distinctly outclassed, and definitely disturbed by the trend of the correspondence. There is no reason, however, for inferring that Bianchini was incompetent. Apparently his scientific equipment derived in large measure from the tradition of the fourteenth-century Paris and Oxford schools (*infra*); cf. L. A. Birkenmajer, *"Flores Almagesti.* Ein angeblich verloren gegangener Traktat Giovanni Bianchini's. . . ." *Bulletin de l'Académie des Sciences de Cracovie,* cl. des sci. math, et naturelles, série A (1911), 268-278.

[31] Besides Burtt, *The Metaphysical Foundation of Modern Physical Science* (New York, 1927) and Strong, *Procedures and Metaphysics* . . . (Berkeley, California, 1936), see Mahnke, *Unendliche Sphäre und Allmittelpunkt,* especially ch. IV, "Die Renaissance des neuplatonischen Pythagoreismus." A controversy of a slightly painful nature has arisen between Mahnke and Walter Pagel, who reviewed *Unendliche Sphäre* in *Isis,* XXX (1930), 121-124. The controversy hinges over the rôle of Jewish influence, especially Ibn Gabirol and the *Cabala,* in the formation of 17th-century mathematical mysticism; Mahnke, "Origins of mathematical mysticism, Erwiderung," with reply by Pagel in *Isis,* XXXII (1940), 131-133; this number of *Isis* has been held in German-occupied Belgium, but a copy of the proof may be consulted at the office of Dr. George Sarton, 189 Widener Library, Cambridge, Mass.

Burtt's thesis has been challenged by Edward W. Strong, who opposes to the vague mathematics of the theorists those solid operational techniques which were being developed by practical men through the study of Euclid. Both Strong and Burtt, it seems to me, present complementary rather than contradictory theses, and both have weakened their cases by ignoring the background of medieval mathematics.

Indeed, the internal elaboration of traditional mathematical material had proceeded rapidly in thirteenth- and fourteenth-century Oxford and Paris.[32] Metamathematics—the hunch that mathematics was the key to all natural knowledge, the pattern of philosophical certitude—had haunted the imagination of Grosseteste, Roger Bacon and Oresme, and the gap between Oresme and

---

See also Ernst Cassirer, "Mathematische Mystik und mathematische Naturwissenschaft," *Lychnos* (Stockholm, 1940), 248-265.

[32] The study of fourteenth-century Paris and Oxford mathematics has scarcely begun. Carl B. Boyer, *The Concepts of the Calculus* (New York, 1939), 69-79, is an interesting beginning, but merely emphasizes the need for editions and special studies of 14th-century texts. An important step in this direction is the project of Marshall Clagett to edit the *Calculationes* of Richard Suiseth. The studies of Ernest A. Moody in late medieval logic should bring out the importance of the new quantitative approach developed at Oxford and transplanted to fifteenth-century Italy. I have prepared a transcription of Oresme's *Questiones super Geometriam Euclidis* from the sole MS, Vat. lat. 2225, ff. 90r-98v, and propose to publish it in connection with his chief mathematico-physical work, the *Tractatus de Configuratione Qualitatum*. This work is discussed in my article, "Nicole Oresme and the Medieval Origins of Modern Science," *Speculum*, XII (1941), 167-185, which contains additional references on the points raised in the present paper. In addition to these references, I might mention Hubert Élie, *Le traité "De l'Infini" de Jean Mair* (Paris, 1937), text and French translation, one of the most important contributions to our slender body of materials for late medieval mathematical philosophy. One of the outstanding *desiderata* in this field is a study of Bradwardine, and modern editions of his *Arithmetica Speculativa* and *Geometria Speculativa*. The mathematical conceptions of both Roger Bacon and his master Grosseteste deserve additional study; in the case of the latter, the projected edition of *Opera Omnia* together with the work of S. H. Thompson should eventually extend our knowledge of his mathematicism and his so-called "Lichtmetaphysik," a term coined, I believe, by Ludwig Baur, and criticized by A. Birkenmaier in his *Études sur Witelo,* Bulletin international de l'Academie Polonaise, cl. de philol., cl. d'hist., et de philos. (1919-1920), 354-360. Miss Mary Welborn is preparing an edition of Grosseteste's *Computus*.

Nicholas of Cusa is very small. Boethian arithmetic and Euclidean geometry had been extended as purely speculative disciplines by Thomas Bradwardine. The classical problems of squaring the circle and duplicating the cube had fascinated the scholastics a century before Cusanus incurred the scorn of Regiomontanus for wasting his time in these aberrations. A set of *Questiones* on the Geometry of Euclid by Nicole Oresme, which I discovered in the Vatican Library, confirms the impression that Pythagorean topics, such as incommensurability, irrationality, and proportionality, were actively, if naively, discussed in the fourteenth-century schools. Theories of the mathematical and physical continuum, of potential and actual infinity, of infinitesimals and infinite series, of fractional exponents[33] and functional variations were elaborated with great subtlety, though not always with strict mathematical rigor, at Paris and Oxford.

Fifteenth-century Italian mathematical theory continues this late scholastic tradition, without apparently introducing any mutational advances.[34] The chief mathematicians of the early Quattrocento, Prosdocimo de' Beldomandi and Blasius of Parma, display little originality, being content to mull over procedures of Bradwardine and Oresme.[35] The graphic technique of representing functional

[33] The first use of fractional exponents is ordinarily credited to Oresme; I understand, however, that an equivalent procedure has been noted in the writings of the English philosopher Dumbleton (by Ernest A. Moody). It also appears in Bianchini's *Flores Almagesti*, referred to above.

[34] P. O. Kristeller and J. H. Randall, Jr., "The Study of the Philosophies of the Renaissance," *Journal of the History of Ideas,* II (1941), 449-496 discuss, in a very suggestive and stimulating fashion, the problem of the introduction of 14th-century Paris and Oxford quantitative logical works into 15th-century Italy. They suggest that this took place through the agency of Paul of Venice about 1400 (493 f.), and precipitated a controversy over Suiseth's *Calculationes* (Cajetan of Thiene). It is apparent that this topic needs careful investigation, since it is crucial in our judgment of the creative rôle of the Quattrocento scientists. Marshall Clagett in his important monograph on *Giovanni Marliani and Late Medieval Physics* (New York, 1941) shows that Marliani, at least, did not understand the terminology of the 14th-century theory of proportionality, as it had been developed by Bradwardine and others.

[35] Beldomandi and Blasius of Parma are discussed in Thorndike's *History of Magic and Experimental Science,* vol. IV, (New York, 1934), ch. 39, with

variations—the so-called *latitudo formarum*—which had been invented by Oresme, was digested into a school text-book which was used in manuscript and printed form both north and south of the Alps. The Euclid of the fifteenth and early sixteenth centuries, the Eculid of the printing presses, was still that of the crabbed medieval manuscripts, the thirteenth century translation and commentary of Campanus of Novara, based ultimately on the twelfth century version of Adelard of Bath.[36] The medieval lore of proportionality[37] was explored by Renaissance artists and artistic theorists—along with the arabico-scholastic science of optics or "perspectiva"—as an aid to the formulation of a mathematical canon of beauty.[38]

The crux of the general case for Italian scientific primacy lies

references to previous literature. But there is need, as Randall and Kristeller point out, for a detailed study of the latter, especially in connection with the controversies over the quantitative vs. the qualitative conception of physics. Despite the careful studies of Wieleitner (referred to in my article on Oresme), the rôle of the *latitudo formarum* in the genesis of analytical geometry has not yet been satisfactorily explored. The treatment of this subject in J. L. Coolidge's *History of Geometrical Methods* (Oxford, 1940), 118, is not sufficient.

[36] A modern edition or at least a critical study of the medieval Euclid is needed. The whole question of the emergence of the concept of geometrical rigor from that of logical rigor, between the fourteenth and the seventeenth centuries, deserves study by someone who is equally competent in the history of logic and of mathematics.

[37] Proportion, a favorite theme of the later medieval scientists, should be treated in its manifold ramifications: music, art, medicine, astronomy; cf. M. F. Bukofzer, "Speculative Thinking in Medieval Music," *Speculum*, XVII (1942), 165-180. On the connection between astronomy and "proportio," Oresme's *De Commensurabilitate motuum coelestium* is a significant text. Oresme's argument from "incommensurability" as evidence of the uncertainty of astrology, appears again in Pico della Mirandola's critique; Thorndike, *Magic and Experimental Science,* IV, 536.

[38] The influence of medieval proportionality and optics on the development of art has been treated by Olschki, *op. cit.,* I, p. 99 ff., p. 183 ff.; but the subject needs further study. The third book of Ghiberti's *Commentaries* is taken directly from the arabico-medieval *Perspectiva,* and other Quattrocento artists, including Piero della Francesca and Leonardo da Vinci, were familiar with the tradition. I have not been able to consult G. ten Doesschate, *De derde Commentaar van Lorenzo Ghiberti in Verband met de middeleeuwsche Optiek,* Academisch proefschrift, (Utrecht, 1940) [reviewed by K. T. A. Halbertsma in *Bijdragen tot de geschiedenis der geneeskunde,* XXI (1941), p. 8].

in the instance of speculative physics.[39] Here the opposition has definitely assumed the burden of proof, and with considerable success. Pierre Duhem undertook to show that the modern era of physics began with the fourteenth-century Paris scholastics, especially Buridan and Oresme, who carried out a fundamental critical revision of the peripatetic theory of motion, establishing in its stead the so-called theory of *impetus*. The limitations of this paper do not allow me to discuss the nature of *impetus* physics. I must confine myself to pointing out that, if Duhem is right, the essential steps in preparing the way for Galileo were taken first in fourteenth-century Paris, and later in sixteenth-century Italy by followers of the Paris tradition, the Quattrocento contributing nothing of importance to this process.[40] The only detailed monographic investigation of fifteenth-century Italian physics—Marshall Clagett's recent study of Giovanni Marliani—tends to substantiate Duhem's contention. On the other hand, criticism from another source has restricted somewhat the rôle of the impetus theory itself. A. Koyré, in his remarkable *Études Galiléennes,* breaks down the develop-

[39] The whole discussion of late medieval and Renaissance physics inevitably centers in the elaboration and critique of Duhem. Clagett's study of Marliani confirms Duhem; Koyré, *Études Galiléennes* (Paris, 1939), qualifies but hardly contradicts. Kristeller and Randall's brief but stimulating discussion of Italian Aristotelianism suggests the lines of a new type of investigation, going beyond, but not necessarily contradicting Duhem. The cross-fertilization of Platonism and Aristotelianism, together with the comprehensive current of Augustinianism in Renaissance scientific thought, appears to be a most promising subject for future investigators. Although not primarily concerned with science, Kristeller's most recent papers suggest lines which the historian of scientific thought may profitably follow: "Florentine Platonism and its Relations with Humanism and Scholasticism," *Church History,* VIII (1939), 201-211; "Augustine and the Renaissance," *International Science* (May, 1941); and his forthcoming monograph on Ficino. [Published New York, Columbia University Press, 1943.—Ed.]

[40] Again an exception might be made for Nicholas of Cusa, whose curious treatise *De Staticis Experimentis* attempts to reduce a wide variety of scientific or pseudo-scientific "experiments" to a simple technique of weighing. The bold conjectural approach of this treatise is reminiscent of the attempt of Oresme to apply his theory of "configuration" to every aspect of natural and supernatural phenomena. It is possible that Cusa may have been more directly influenced by Oresme than has been supposed; cf. Durand, "Nicole Oresme," 184 f.

ment of the theory of motion into three distinct phases: 1) the peripatetic, which was taken over almost intact in thirteenth-century scholasticism, 2) the late scholastic modification of peripatetic dynamics, the theory of *impetus,* which remained current until the middle of the sixteenth century, 3) the modern phase, based on the renewed studies of Archimedes and on the epoch-making experiments and intuitions of Galileo. The advance marked by each of these last two stages is likened by Koyré to an intellectual mutation, and it is from him that I have adopted that phrase as used in this paper. Koyré, then, substantiates Duhem at least in this respect: he attributes absolute originality to the fourteenth-century Paris school, while implicitly denying it to that of fifteenth-century Italy.

One point, however, may be raised by the advocates of Italian "primato": was not the reception of Archimedes,[41] which made possible the advance beyond the theory of *impetus,* itself the work of the Quattrocento? Must not this reception, like that of Ptolemy's *Geography,* be credited to humanistic science? The answer is fairly clear: unlike the *Geographia,* the bulk of Archimedes' works had been available to the West in the latter part of the Middle Ages—rendered into Latin by the great Dominican translator, William of Moerbeke. On the other hand they had lain almost completely dormant, presumably for the simple reason that they were much too difficult for the scholastics to master. The revival of interest in Archimedes came about in the sixteenth century because the scientific world was ready for it. That revival was not primarily the work of humanists. It is true that a new humanistic translation had been made about 1460 by Jacobus of Cremona, using the same manuscript as William of Moerbeke. That translation was revised by Regiomontanus, who planned to publish it together with the Greek original, but he died before being able to carry out his project; there is no evidence from Regiomontanus' own works that he had absorbed the mathematics and physics of Archimedes. The earliest

[41] The influence of Archimedes in the Middle Ages, though unquestionably slight, might prove on close examination to be more significant than has usually been supposed. Koyré's *Études Galiléennes* throw much light on the rôle of Archimedes in 16th-century physics.

printed editions were based on the Moerbeke text, braze ly plagiarized by Luca Gaurico (1503) and Niccolo Tartaglia (1543). In 1544 the Greek original and the Regiomontanus version of Jacobus' translation were published at Basel. It was not until 1558 that a really satisfactory Latin version became available—the work of Federigo Commandino—and it is from this event, presumably, that the "mutation" of physical theory must be dated.

## CONCLUSION

The composite balance sheet of the departments of Quattrocento science examined in this paper does not appear to present a clear and uniform Italian advantage. Owing to very broad historical circumstances, especially to the disastrous Hundred Years War coming on top of the Black Death, both England and France undoubtedly slumped in creative vigor. Germany and Italy, enjoying relative peace, order and prosperity, rose in cultural distinction. Bologna, Florence, and Padua, Erfurt, Nuremberg and Vienna replaced Oxford and Paris as the outstanding scientific centers. The diversity of social life, the wide basis of economic prosperity in her cities, permitted Italy to cultivate a greater variety of disciplines and arts than could have been found during the same period in the north. Nevertheless it does not appear that she was uncontestedly supreme in any of those fields examined in this paper. Antecedents in scholastic tradition have been found for nearly all her scientific achievements. Apart from Leonardo da Vinci[42]—who belongs at least in part to the early Cinquecento—and Nicholas of Cusa—who might be described as an "extravagant" of the Quattrocento, and who in any case was not an Italian—the only individual of marked

---

[42] The omission of Leonardo from this discussion may seem somewhat arbitrary. It is justified, however, by the fact that Leonardo can be regarded as a transition figure standing between the Quattrocento and the High Renaissance. His scientific achievement marks the culmination of the late medieval tradition—as Duhem has shown—and at the same time ushers in the brilliant sixteenth-century Italian tradition leading from Benedetti and Cardan to Galileo.

scientific genius was Toscanelli, and it is doubtful whether any mutational advances may be attributed to him, except perhaps in the field of cartography. The increments of classical knowledge through translation and discovery appear to have been slender in the fields of cosmology, mathematics and physics.[43] Cross-fertilization from abroad, on the other hand, appears to have been highly stimulating, whether this took place through the agency of the Church, the universities, or the patronage of republics or despotisms.

The chief increments of knowledge—or units of innovation—must be classed as internal elaboration of traditional material, rather than as mutations. Some historians who have admitted a partial continuity of subject-matter between medieval and Quattrocento thought have credited the latter with a new approach or spirit, a greater strenuousness, consistency, rigor, a revolutionary insight which amounted to a creation *ex nihilo,* a decisive jump in the course of progress. Claims of originality based upon an intangible spirit are not, of course, subject to absolute proof or disproof. Yet such would seem to be the basis for much of the case for a comprehensive Quattrocento "primato." The evidence, as I see it, points to a qualified estimate, an estimate which satisfies the two

[43] A complete bibliography of Renaissance scientific translations is much to be desired, as a preliminary to a comparison of the relative rôles of humanistic and scholastic translations in Renaissance science. In addition to the humanistic translations already mentioned, the following might also be cited: Ptolemy's *Quadripartitum* by Jacopo d'Angelo; a Latin translation of Archimedes attributed to Aurispa; Theophrastus *De Plantis* by Theodore of Gaza; Aristotle, *Mechanical Problems* by Theodore of Gaza; *Problemata, Historia Animalium* by both Gaza and George of Trebizond, *De Generatione et Corruptione* by Andronicus Callistus, and *De Caelo* by Joannes Argyropulos; Alexander of Aphrodisias, *Problems,* by Theodore of Gaza. In the field of medicine the rediscovery of Celsus *De Medicina* (Guarino, 1426) exerted considerable influence, but could hardly be described as mutational. Indeed, except in the rather restricted fields of botany and geography, it is difficult to see a single instance in which the humanist translators of the Quattrocento provided the basis for a radical scientific advance. On the other hand, a real advance in the field of "natural philosophy" appears to have been introduced through the rediscovery of Lucretius (Poggio, 1417); cf. Max Lehnerdt, *Lucretius in der Renaissance* (Königsberg, 1904); H. Pflaum, *Die Idee der Liebe: Leone Ebreo,* (Tübingen, 1926), 42-45. The influence of Epicureanism, in both its medieval and its Renaissance form, needs further investigation by historians of science.

cardinal articles of the historian's faith: continuity and spontaneity in historical process. That estimate in this case may be put as follows: the balance of tradition and innovation in fifteenth-century Italy was not so decisively favorable as to distinguish that century radically from those that preceded it, nor to constitute the Quattrocento a unique and unrivaled moment in the history of western thought.

*Arturo Castiglioni*

# THE MEDICAL SCHOOL AT PADUA
# AND THE RENAISSANCE
# OF MEDICINE*

Among the first universities which arose in Italy at the beginning of
the thirteenth century, and slowly organized on the lines of the
ancient Latin schools of the Empire, taking certainly as model in
Medicine the Salernitan school, which was the first lay medical
school of which we know the organization, Padua is perhaps the
one which most surely and rapidly affirms a spirit of independence
which sometimes assumes the character of a revolutionary tendency. The intellectual tendency of the University has a well-defined
characteristic note: the little university was formed at its beginning
by a group of students when the Princes of Carrara dominated the
town. In the year 1222 a few students of Bologna abandoned the
school of law of this town which seems to have been already well
organized and migrated to Padua, bringing with them some of their
teachers, as had happened some years before when a group of students had chosen the town of Vicenza as their seat of learning. At
that time and still more in the following century the University was
much more bound to the scholars and to the teachers than to the
city: Universitas meant exactly a community of students who chose
their masters and then formed an independent organization. These

* The Nathan Lewis Hatfield Lecture, XII, read before the College of Phy-
sicians of Philadelphia, November 29, 1933. Reprinted from *Annals of
Medical History*, n.s., Vol. II (1935), pp. 214-27, with the permission of
Paul B. Hoeber, Inc. The illustrations in the original article are omitted.

men who considered study as the principal aim of their lives let themselves be easily induced to change their residence, going where the conditions of life were more favorable, the protection of the Commune and of the Princes more efficacious, the safety of life greater and the kindness of the citizen more cordial. In many cases the students were attracted and enticed from the one or the other town with promises of particular privileges, of exemption from the taxes, of excellent teachers. Thus in 1228 Vercelli, which was a little town in Piedmont, sent to Padua its representatives to invite the students with the largest promises to come there. From the document witnessing this fact, which is still preserved, one can see that in the year 1228 four groups of students already existed, divided according to their nationality: the first of Latins of the langue d'oil (that is to say French and Normans), the other of Latins of langue d'oc (Provencals, Spaniards and Catalans), one of Germans and one of Italians. In this time the students must have been a great number, because the town of Vercelli promised to find for them 500 lodgings and more if it should be necessary.

During the whole thirteenth century the prosperity of the University of Padua increased in spite of the menaces of the Emperors and of the Popes who were often in conflict with the town: the corporations of students were sometimes only two: Transalpini or Ultramontani and Cisalpini or Citramontani.

This division according to Nationality was for some centuries the only recognized and perfectly ordered: not until the beginning of the fourteenth century was the universitas artistarum medicinae, physicae et naturae constituted as a faculty which collected all students of natural sciences and of medicine, with rights equal to those of the universitas juristarum, the faculty of law. But the medical teaching had been organized from 1250 at which time two chairs of medicine were established. In 1262 the chairs of medicine were three and the tendency to entrust different professors with the teaching was more and more manifest. In early times the teachers were elected by the students, but this gave origin to such tumults that the elections began to be made by the State, and at the end of the fourteenth century professors were appointed only in this way. During the thirteenth century when the Arabistic current became stronger in Italy, and in literature, in art, and in science was felt the effect of the penetration into Italy of the ideas which had arisen in the great centers of culture of Islam, and the western world received from them through the Arabian commentators and the Jewish translators, unknown writings of Aristotle, Tolomeus* and Galen, and when the dawn of the Renaissance of classical studies, which had later a stronger impulse, began, when with the fall of Constantinople some eminent Greek scholars came to Venice and spread the study of the Greek language, Padua had already the name of an Averroistic university, almost in opposition to Bologna which was essentially scholastic.

In Padua at the beginning of the thirteenth century taught Pietro d'Abano (1250-1316), a physician and philosopher who was one of the most eminent scholars of this time and who with his vast literary and scientific lore dominated the whole learning of this epoch. He attempted to resolve with syllogisms the contradictions which arose between the medicine of the Arabic authors and speculative philosophy; he endeavored to prepare a complete treatise of theoretical and practical medicine in which all tendencies should be reconciled and the scholars could be informed both concerning that natural philosophy which in the opinion of the author was the pivot of all sciences, and concerning diseases and their remedies. An Averroist in his ideas, a dialectician in form, in his book "Conciliator controversiarum quae inter philosophos et medicos versantur," from which he had the name and the fame of a conciliator, he stated all problems as dialectical queries and solved them so that in almost every case the empirical proofs were overcome by the syllogism. And yet through the farrago of these philosophical discussions the acute observation of a man of genius is apparent. His true master in medicine was Avicenna: in his studies on the soul Pietro was generally faithful to the ideas of Averroes, but sometimes he contended against Aristotle and Averroes at the same

* [Ptolemy.—Ed.]

time; doubtless he showed himself a man who was able to detach himself from the classics and to discuss the authority of the greatest of them.

Pietro d'Abano was one of the first and strongest defenders of the Italic Averroism in which one must recognize the rebellion against the yoke of theologizing philosophy. Averroism collects some ideas and tendencies deriving from the great Arabian physicians and particularly and above all the thesis of the common intellective soul of the human species. One should not forget that Averroism means first Arabism, and then all those who had drunk at the Arabic sources and accepted the authority of the great Commentator of Aristotle.

The influence exercised by Pietro through his teaching and his books, some of which were considered till the end of the fourteenth century as very authoritative texts, was certainly deep and vast, and even Dante who lived at Padua at this time and probably was one of his pupils, felt his influence. The name of this physician and philosopher, who had gone to Constantinople in order to study Greek and to read Galen and Aristotle in the original texts, and the fame of this scholar, who had taught medicine in Paris and had been considered there as one of the greatest masters, were diffused through the whole of Italy. His fame moreover was perhaps increased by the news of the persecutions by the Dominican friars who had accused him of heresy because of forty-five propositions contained in his work which were considered contrary to Christian dogma. When he was called to the city of Padua, and became in the year 1306 professor of medicine at the University, his name was already well known to all who dedicated their studies to philosophical researches. An eminent physician, he very soon became a celebrated practitioner and was consulted by Pope Honorius IV and the Marquis Azzo d'Este. The crowd of students who came to attend his lectures was so numerous that Gentile da Foligno, one of the great surgeons of this time, when he came before the hall where the master was teaching, fell on his knees crying out: "Hail, holy temple!"

During the thirteenth century the study of medicine flourished in all the universities of Italy and while in Bologna with the teaching of Mondino de'Luzzi the new travail of anatomic thought was beginning, and the first surgeons, heirs of the Salernitan teaching, were taking their first steps towards the institution of the new surgery, Padua became at the end of the century the most important center of epidemiologic studies. The pestilence, which about the middle of the twelfth century had devastated Italy, taught the necessity of defensive measures, particularly for the sea towns which drew their wealth from the over-sea trade; and as early as the year 1374 Venice forbade entrance into the town of infected or simply suspected persons and goods. Ragusa published at first by-laws concerning quarantine; and very soon, at about the end of the century, Venice collected all the measures against pestilence in an exemplary sanitary legislation. To this end the contribution of the great masters of the Paduan university was very precious. Among these teachers Pietro da Tossignano, author of the renowned advice against pestilence, was one of the most famous; but the most authoritative was doubtless Gentile da Foligno, who had been called in 1337 by Count Ubertino di Carrara to teach medicine at the university. He was called "the soul of Avicenna" and his advice had the greatest diffusion. Genoa, and the towns of Tuscany and of middle Italy took counsel with him in difficult cases.

In the thirteenth century there is an important development in the study of anatomy: Pope Sixtus IV gave official permission to dissect, and Alessandro Benedetti, a teacher of anatomy in Padua about the end of the century, published a treatise on anatomy in five books and 138 chapters, affirming the necessity of anatomical dissection independent of the custom, generally accepted till that time, of conceding to the school only the corpses of executed persons. To him we owe the construction of the anatomical theater where he delivered his first lectures; to Antonio Benivieni, the merit of having been the first forerunner of Morgagni, with his important observations in the field of pathological anatomy, to which he brought an important contribution of exact observations.

At the end of the thirteenth century flourished in Padua the study of botany, which became the foundation of all later researches in the field of natural sciences. Among the humanistic authors who held Pliny in great honor, two deserve to be particularly noted: Giorgio Valla, a Latinist of great worth, a deep scholar in classical literature, who conferred elegance upon scientific language, and Ermolao Barbaro, an eminent philosopher, who endeavored to restore the text of Pliny and wrote a commentary on Dioscorides.

The life of this man, who can be considered as the prince of the humanists of this time, deserves really to be quoted: he was crowned poet laureate in his fourteenth year by Frederic III, took his degree in Padua in 1477; translated and published some books of Aristotle, held public office, taught the Greek language and literature, and had in his home gatherings of the most celebrated scientists of his time. He was in 1486 ambassador of the Republic of Venice to the Emperor Frederick, and in 1489 ambassador to Pope Innocent VIII, who created him Patriarch of Aquileia and Cardinal. He died in 1493, not yet forty years old, leaving some works which reveal an astonishing erudition and a perfect knowledge of the Greek language and literature and of classic antiquity.

Thus we find about the end of the thirteenth century the first bud of the renaissance of medicine, which flourished contemporaneously with the renaissance of philosophy, of letters and of art, in the most brilliant period of Italian history, when the university, especially through secular work of patient researches, opened its doors to the new doctrines which tended to deliver science from its bonds.

The return to the old texts, begun by the Italians who had never lost contact with the Greek spirit, ardently supported by the humanists, rendered the relations of the western world with the Hellenism more intimate. While on one hand the return of the old Greek and Latin authors in their original form seemed at the beginning to strengthen their authority and to make criticism of them more difficult, on the other hand the Italians discovered in the old texts those sane reasonings, keen observation, and freedom of inquiry and criticism, which for too long a time seemed to have been forgotten. One begins to understand in Italy that more than the maxims of the ancients, the spirit which dictated them is admirable: the Italian spirit comes little by little nearer to the thought of the ancient classics and to the form of their literature; and I believe that it is essentially from this humanism that free and fruitful criticism, objective and impartial is born, which grows with individuality in medicine and in art, with the desire to see new things and to think with one's own brain instead of accepting supinely the dogmatic affirmations of the school. In the spirit of humanism the foremost factor of the renaissance of medicine has to be sought; a renaissance which was in preparation during the last centuries of the Middle Ages with the studies of anatomy, with the first clinical observations, with that love of nature which is characteristic of the Renaissance.

At the end of the century another factor of great importance contributes to prepare the new times, that is the invention of printing. To this epoch belong the first printed and partly illustrated texts of medicine, and in order to imagine what a change the diffusion of printing brought also in the field of medical culture it suffices to remember that as late as in 1395 the University of Paris possessed only some few manuscript books of medicine.

The part which Venice and the Venetian printers had in the diffusion of medical culture is noteworthy. We must recall that in the last decade of the fifteenth century two hundred Venetian printers published 1500 works, more than all the other printers in the whole of Italy. We must recall that to this epoch belong the first anatomical figures, and that it is probable that the sight of the first drawings, in some old reproductions of the five or six figures which represented the osseous, arterial and venous systems and were derived from Arabian and Persian manuscripts, had demonstrated their inexactness and made it necessary to replace them little by little with figures based on the examination of the corpse. Certainly the first old anatomic figures of the old handwritten texts, so plain in the ingenuousness of their lines, showed more evidently their errors and demonstrated that correction was necessary: perhaps it was thanks to the old drawings that the initiative for anatomical teaching through the figure arose, to which another fact gave an extraordinary impulse: the renaissance of the Hellenistic conception according to which disease is only a disturbed harmony which it behooves Nature to cure.

In this time of the renaissance of the conception of life, Padua was the only school in which freedom of research and of teaching was granted. In Padua Andreas Vesalius, who had been educated at Louvain and studied medicine at Montpellier and Paris and taught anatomy in Louvain, became in 1537 professor of anatomy. In Padua where the university, owing to the intelligent care of the magistrates of the Republic, was at this time in its greatest splendor, and where from every part of Europe scholars came as to the most renowned center of learning, Vesalius found that possibility of free research, that comprehension of his work and of his courageous criticism which rendered it possible for him to accomplish a work which seemed in his time to be incredibly audacious. The chief task of his life was to renew the teaching of the anatomy of the human body and to overthrow the teaching of Galen, which during sixteen centuries had not only prevailed but been considered indisputable. He demonstrated that the studies of Galen were based only upon animal dissections, and that all that concerned the human body had been hardly observed. He taught from the same chair from which all teachers had bowed to the high authority of the great master of Pergamon, that he had made hundreds of errors, and that it was necessary to begin again the study of anatomy. It was certainly excessive daring for a young man of hardly twenty-five years, and the struggle was very sharp; but Vesalius knew how to carry it, perfectly sure of the truth of his ideas, animated only by the conviction of the absolute necessity of clearing the field from all ancient superstitions. He was also in first place the great and courageous reformer of pictorial anatomic representation: in Padua some great artists, such as Mantegna, one of the first realistic painters of corpses, and Riccio, the exquisite sculptor who reproduced in his fine bronzes with perfect fidelity the forms and the muscles of men and animals, had certainly exercised their influence on the development of anatomical thought. Riccio was a great friend of the anatomist Marcantonio Della Torre and sculptured for this family of physicians in the Church of St. Fermo in Verona a magnificent monument, the bas-reliefs of which, at present preserved in the Louvre, belong to the best works of Italian Renaissance. Vesalius understood clearly the importance of adorning his book with the best drawings: he supervised with the greatest care those who worked for his book and to whom he probably indicated himself, the object of the drawings. He complained in his letters of the trouble they had caused him, and found as collaborator one of the best pupils of Titian, Jan Stephan Kalkar, a Flemish painter whose paintings were often difficult to distinguish from those of his master. Probably Kalkar engraved the pictures on wood: certainly the figures are executed with perfect truthfulness and with great taste, chiefly from dissections of youthful bodies. The drawings are free and bold and in the book of Vesalius we find for the first time in a text for students a clear representation of true facts in the most beautiful form.

Thus under the protection of an intelligent and strong government which considered the university as one of the most important instruments of its political power, in this fertile ground, modern anatomy, as Leonardo had imagined it in his solitary work, was born. In a time in which in the German universities anatomical teaching was not yet regular and when in Flanders Vesalius himself was compelled to undertake some adventurous expeditions with his students to steal the corpses of executed persons and thus make dissections possible, and when the great anatomist was persecuted at the Court of Spain by the enemies of his affirmations, Padua was the center of experimental science. When Vesalius set out on a pilgrimage to Jerusalem and received a call from the Venetian Senate to reoccupy the chair of anatomy, his greatest longing was to come back to the town which to him seemed "the only nurse of high genius."

But not alone because Vesalius was one of her great teachers and because in Padua his immortal book was written and the anatomical figures designed, does Padua deserve the first place in the history of the scientific renaissance in Italy. Before and after Vesalius Padua had among its professors some of the most excellent anatomists of all times. Here taught Gabrielle Falloppio who was certainly the most courageous of the innovators and the most illustrious of the Italian anatomists of this century. He departed even more decisively than Vesalius from the teaching of Galen. He corrected the descriptions by Vesalius of the anatomy of the cerebral arteries and of the clitoris: he described the tubes that bear his name, the oculomotor muscles, the cerebral nerves, the chorda tympani, the semicircular canals and the aqueduct. The first edition of "Observationes anatomicae" was published in Venice in 1651.

His pupil was Girolamo Fabrizio d'Acquapendente (1537-1619) who studied particularly the anatomy and physiology of the uterus and of the fetus. To him was due the creation of a new anatomical theater at Padua, which is still preserved. He was the author of an important study on the physiology of respiration and of the voice, and it is curious that he once treated this subject so profoundly that it is told that one day, in 1588, all the students of German nationality deserted his school, thinking that in the explanation of the mechanism of the muscles of the tongue he mocked their pronunciation of Italian. He studied not less deeply the physiology of the circulation and was the discoverer of the valves of the veins. He was the teacher of Harvey and in the hall of the old Paduan university, where the coat-of-arms of the most illustrious students are painted, we find that of Guglielmo Harvey, belonging to the Natio Anglica: a burning candle between two snakes of Aesculapius. That was the time in which from the whole of Europe strangers came to Padua to learn anatomy: a pupil of Falloppio was Volcher Voiter, born at Gröningen in 1534, died in 1600, whose works are important for the development of the anatomy of the human fetus and the child. A pupil of the Paduan school of anatomy was the Spaniard Juan Valverde di Hamuzco, who published a manual of anatomy in Spanish which had a great circulation. Of this anatomical school Haller could justly write: for a century and a half it was the leader of all Europe, so that there were but few dissectors who did not come from its halls.

The studies of physiology began in Italy with the Renaissance and many of them were devoted to the circulation of the blood, among which were those of Realdo Colombo, successor to Vesalius in the chair of anatomy at Padua, who in 1558 published a work in which he affirmed the non-existence of the passages through the septum of the heart between the right and left ventricle, belief in which up to that time had been generally accepted. He clearly stated that the arteria venosa (pulmonary vein) carried blood and not air and he indicated the greater circulation in a general way. He was the teacher of the greatest physiologist of this period, Andrea Cesalpino, a physician and a philosopher, born in Arezzo in 1519, who attacked one of the most important of the errors of the Galenic concept, namely, the inclusion of the liver in the greater circulation. He was the first to use the word "circulation" (1559) and observed what happened in the veins after a ligature had been placed about the arm. His discovery is the essential basis for the doctrine of the circulation of the blood which was later completed and clearly described by Harvey.

Thus the most important and decisive of the problems of physiology, whose solution marked the fall of the Galenic conception, found at the University of Padua its foremost workers: from Colombo to Cesalpino, from Fabrizio d'Acquapendente to Harvey. In a magnificent collaboration which had been hitherto without example the work of anatomy and physiology of scientists of different nations had prepared in Padua the triumph of exact sciences.

But clinical sciences very rapidly followed this movement. To this century belong the first studies of psychiatry of Giovanni Battista Da Monte who devoted his attention to melancholy and other forms of nervous diseases while Girolamo Mercuriale, a great teacher also in the field of hygiene and of medical gymnastics, endeavored to classify them according to the etiology; in Padua began the teaching of pharmacology which drew great advantage from the institution of the so-called garden of simples, of which the oldest was founded in Padua by Francesco Buonafede in 1545. Clinical teaching was initiated at the end of this century by Giovanni Battista Da Monte at the bedside of the patient. From this teaching in Padua the clinical teaching of the University of Leyden arose. Evald Schrevelius and Jan van Heurne, who had been scholars at Padua, brought this method of teaching to Holland where medicine throve in a free and very rich country which seemed to inherit in the seventeenth century the fortunes of the Venetian Republic and its part in the progress of science, just as it snatched from Venice, after the discovery of the new trade routes, the domination of the seas.

The most interesting figure of the Paduan Renaissance is surely that of Girolamo Fracastoro, a man of genius who was in Padua a comrade of Nicolaus Copernicus, a pupil of the great anatomist Achillini and a friend of Cardinal Pietro Bembo, the great humanist. Pathological conceptions had a very important evolution during the Renaissance, due to the fact that in this epoch certain diseases spread through Italy which up to then had been but little known: smallpox, chickenpox, influenza and typhus. In the sixteenth century syphilis spread all through Italy in the form of an epidemic disease which claimed many victims.

This is not the place to take up the much discussed historical question as to the origin of syphilis; that is, whether it was brought to Europe through Spain after the discovery of America or had already existed in Europe in milder forms. It is certain that it was spread through Italy more extensively than through other European countries and was closely studied and efficiently treated. Girolamo Fracastoro was the most illustrious among the many physicians who dedicated their study to the pathology of syphilis. He wrote a poem, which was considered during the Renaissance as the most beautiful poetical work in Latin verse, worthy to be compared with the poems of the Golden Age of Latin literature. This poem, entitled "Syphilis sive Morbus Galicus," which was published in Verona in 1530, had an enormous and widespread publicity. The name of the disease is taken from this poem, in which Fracastoro told the story of a shepherd, called Syphilus, who contracted the terrible disease as a punishment from Apollo. He gives an exact description of the disease, prescribing the use of mercury and guaiac in its treatment.

The most important work of Fracastoro, although it is not to this book that he owes his greatest reputation, was the "De contagione et contagiosis morbis," published in 1546 at Venice, which is by far the most valuable example of his scientific value. Fracastoro was the father of modern epidemiology and was the first to study epidemic diseases in the light of scientific concepts, distinguishing three forms of infection and contagion. These were contagion by direct contact, such as scabies, leprosy, etc.; contagion by indirect contact by means of fomites, such as clothing, sheets, etc., which are carriers of the germs of the contagion and thus spread the diseases; and finally a third form in which the disease could be transmitted at a distance without direct contact, such as plague, smallpox and similar diseases. In such cases he imagined that the germs were propagated by selecting the humors for which they have the greatest affinity, entering the organism by means of the respiration. The germs (seminaria) were then thought to be absorbed from the breath and adhered to those humors which carried them to the heart. These germs according to Fracastoro had the power of multiplying rapidly. Those that infected animals could not infect plants, and vice versa, and there were even certain diseases confined to man or to certain animals; certain diseases had even special affinities for certain individuals or organs. Hence it is apparent from these statements that Fracastoro had a clear insight into the specific characteristics of contagion and should be considered as one of the important precursors of the modern doctrine of infection.

Among the diseases which appeared for the first time in Italy or rather were first studied in this century was typhus fever. In a Parmese diary of 1477 there is described an epidemic with high fever and exanthems, which was probably typhoid fever; also the so-called Merranic plague which spread through Italy from 1492 to

1493, as can be learned from the writings of the Jews banished from Spain. The first clinical description of this disease we owe to Fracastoro who in his classic book on contagious diseases described it with accuracy, distinguishing it from bubonic plague and typhoid fever.

The pathology of tuberculosis was also studied by Fracastoro, who maintained the contagiousness of the disease and the possibility that it might also be spread by means of the clothing and bed linen. This concept guided Fracastoro in prescribing prophylactic measures in the fight against tuberculosis: he forbade the use of purges or of substances which hindered expectoration. In all his work it can be clearly seen how modern scientific epidemiology had its origin in the outstanding writings of Girolamo Fracastoro.

Contemporaneously Italian surgery made great progress in this century, and also in this field Padua had some of the best known surgeons as teachers. Among these it will suffice to mention the names of Fabrizio d'Acquapendente, the anatomist, who enjoyed the fame of being the greatest Italian surgeon of his time, and Giovanni Antonio Della Croce who published in Venice in 1573 a book which had a widespread sale, and was considered the classical text on surgery for more than two centuries. The description of trepanning in cases of wounds of the skull forms an important chapter of this book in which all instruments which are necessary for these operations are reproduced.

This scientific movement of progress in all fields of medicine, of which I have endeavored to give a picture in its most important expressions, found its climax when at the beginning of the fifteenth century, Padua being ahead of the scientific progress, the gigantic figure of a man arose who impressed on the whole historic epoch the mark of his individuality. Galileus Galilei, discovering the telescope and the microscope, gave two mighty weapons to research and was the founder of experimental science.

At the time in which a great passion for studies, a great love of beauty, and inexhaustible desire for glory vivified all the works of the Italians, Padua was the most important center of scientific research. Here came teachers and students from all parts of Europe, here the astronomers searched the secret of the stars, the physicians the mystery of life, the mathematicians the most difficult problems of geometry and of algebra: from Copernicus to Galileus, from Vesalius to Fabrizio d'Acquapendente, from Colombo to Fracastoro, physicians, politicians, lawyers, physicists, naturalists and mathematicians prepared and accomplished the Renaissance of Science. In Padua the great international currents met; the farseeing protection of a wise government preserved the freedom of teaching and of learning as a great treasure.

How important a part foreign students had in the life of the university and particularly in the school of medicine, is demonstrated by the books of the foreign nations in which their Consiliarii noted the most important happenings. Sometimes the representative of the students complained before the authorities because the lectures were not regularly delivered. In the year 1587 a few national groups were represented in the Natio Alemanna, that is the students from Switzerland, Bohemia, Denmark, Flanders and Poland, and each group chose its representative. The Consiliarius of the Natio Alemanna had the right to hold the matricular book and he had first place in all the ceremonies of the university, two votes in all meetings and the right to bear the sword. The English students were so numerous that in 1534 the Natio Anglica divided itself from the Scota: in 1603 the English, the Scotch and the Irish are again united in the English nation. This nation had its own councillor, a beadle and a secretary (*cancellarius*); it possessed also its own library and special privileges.

The influence of Padua on English medicine during the Renaissance is undoubtedly very important. I do not know whether it is really possible to limit the Italian influence on English scholarship to a definite period of time, that is from the beginning to the end of the fifteenth century, as Lewis Einstein[1] thinks; surely throughout the whole Renaissance we find in English literature many quotations

[1] Einstein, L. The Italian Renaissance in England. New York, Columbia Univ. Press.

which demonstrate that at the Paduan school British scholars were very common. Many Oxford men crossed the Alps during the fifteenth century: Vicenza and Vercelli had English rectors: the new spirit of the Renaissance had effected a revolution in the intellectual world, and Oxonians went to Italy in search of the new Humanism. I may mention one of the most renowned of the English scholars of Italian Universities: John Tiptoft, Earl of Worcester, who was known in the whole of Italy for his scholarship and was considered, as Einstein says, the first example of an "Italianate Englishman." He had gone to Padua to continue his Latin studies and he is said to have caused Pius the Second to weep with joy at hearing such eloquence flow from English lips. Thomas Linacre came to Italy in 1488, became in Florence the friend of Lorenzo dei Medici and of Politian, graduated as a doctor of medicine at Padua and called Italy "Sancta mater studiorum." He was the first great Humanist and the foremost physician of his time, and was considered by Erasmus the introducer of medical science into England. In London he became Court physician with John Chamber, who had also studied medicine at Padua. He was the founder of the College of Physicians in London modelled on Italian institutions.

The efforts of the group of Oxonian scholars at Padua succeeded in establishing the new learning at Oxford and in extending the Italian influence in England. The famous Doctor Caius had also been a scholar at Padua and he founded at Cambridge a Medical College, which still bears his name.

The reputation of Padua as a center of learning was popular in England from old times.[2] Geoffrey Chaucer, who was in Lombardy on a diplomatic mission about 1372, quotes Padua in the prologue to "The Clerkes Tale":

> I wol you telle a tale which that I
> Lerned at Padowe of a worthy clerk. . . .
> Franceys Petrark, the laureat poete.

[2] Spielman, M. H. The Iconography of Andrus Vesalius, 1514-1564. London, 1925.

Every alumnus at Padua prided himself upon his academic distinction and defended his peculiar Latinity. George Chapman in his comedy "All Fools" lets Costanza say:

You have a younger son at Padua
I like his learning well—make him your heir.

In the first scene of "The Taming of the Shrew" Shakespeare pays his tribute to Padua. Lucentio explains the motive of his journey:

For the great desire I had
To see fair Padua, nursery of Arts . . .
I am arrived . . .
And haply institute
A course of Learning and ingenious studies
And therefore Tranio . . . I have Pisa left,
And am to Padua come, as he that leaves
A shallow plash to plunge him in the deep.

But the fame of Padua as a center of learning did not cease with the end of the Renaissance. It may be of some interest to quote here the first contact of one of the most prominent American physicians with the Paduan School. John Morgan, born in Philadelphia in 1735, where he received the degree of A.B. from the College of Philadelphia in 1757, went to Europe in 1760 to pursue his medical study. He spent five years in Europe and when he came back to Philadelphia delivered his famous "Discourse upon the Institution of Medical Schools in America" (1765), which was the most important contribution to the foundation of medical schools in the United States. In his "Journal" he tells of his visit to Morgagni, in July 1764. Morgagni showed him many interesting preparations, told him of his new discoveries and

. . . He was so good as to do me the honour of making me a present of his late publication, two volumes in folio "De sedibus et causis morborum," of which there have been three different editions within the three years, being in the highest estimation throughout all Europe, and all copies of the late edition already bought up.

Very noteworthy is the importance in Padua of the Polish students, especially in the sixteenth century when after the spread of the Reformation in Germany it was necessary for the Polish students to go to Italy in order to complete their studies. Between the years 1544 and 1550 a great part of the teachers of the university of Cracow went to Padua, leaving their schools; a Polish historian notices that often there is to be found in the acts of episcopacies of this time, near the name of certain high clergymen, the remark "Proficiens in Italiam studii gratia" (gone to Italy in order to study). In the high places of the kingdom only those who had studied at Padua could be accepted, and we can calculate that the number of Polish students in Padua in the second half of this century was more than 1500. Nicolaus Copernicus, the great astronomer, was a student at Padua from 1501 to 1504 and regularly matriculated in the Faculty of medicine; there seems to be little doubt that the discovery of the heliocentric system of the Universe can be dated from Padua.

Padua was the foremost school for non-Catholic students to whom inscription in the university of Cracow was forbidden. The greatest Polish physicians of the Renaissance were pupils of the Paduan university: Joseph Struthius, who was physician of the King Sigmond August of Holland and was considered one of the most learned men of that country, was one of the most illustrious Paduan pupils.

Not less important was the part of French students; Monsieur de Montaigne tells us in his diary that in 1580 more than 100 French gentlemen lived in Padua in order to frequent the schools.

The government of the Republic defended with the greatest authority the rights of the students who could freely send embassies to the Doge of Venice. When Pope Pius IV published the Bull "In sacrosancta" which prohibited non-Catholic students from obtaining the degree in medicine which was then conferred in church and in the presence of the ecclesiastical authorities, the graduate taking the oath on the gospel, the Republic instituted the conferment of degree by the authority of the college of physicians, and to the energetic protest made by the Vatican, Venice answered through Fra' Paolo Sarpi, the renowned scientist and Councilor of the Republic, that it was not thought necessary that an excellent physician should be profound in theology.

The old Paduan University had thus assumed with great dignity a political function. It had seen the transformation of the hall of an old inn called Il Bo', namely at the Sign of the Bull, a name which among the university students is current to this very day, into the magnificent historical hall in which thousands of inscriptions and coats of arms tell the stories of masters and students. At the end of the sixteenth century a great international current started from Padua to all the important centers of culture in the world.

The bright epoch began in Padua with the work of Pietro d'Abano, a physician and philosopher, had its climax with Andreas Vesalius and Girolamo Fracastoro, the founders of anatomy and pathology, and closed with the work of Galileo. These physicians of the Renaissance, who were at the same time humanists, men of letters and artists, saw with prophetic mind the solution of the great problems of life; the great blind man whose doctrines were solemnly condemned by the High Court of the Holy Office of the Inquisition in Rome had seen beyond his time and beyond the limits of human knowledge; he affirmed that the laws of nature are written in mathematical characters and that in order to achieve the truth it is first necessary to put experience before any discussion. From the Padua of the Renaissance, from the university where anatomical and physiological teaching had had the most important success, the beginning of experimental science was initiated.

*Henry Morley*

# ANDREAS VESALIUS*

There is an old folio, known to all who have visited the fountain-heads of medical literature, and dear to bookworms for its woodcut illustrations, which in their own time were ascribed to Titian. It is the "Corporis Humani Fabrica" of Andreas Vesalius. The first page is adorned with a large and spirited woodcut, in which a young man, wearing professor's robes, is to be seen standing at the table of a lecture theatre, and pointing out from a robust subject that lies before him the inner secrets of the human body. The tiers of benches that surround the lecture table are crowded with grave doctors, who are leaning forward, struggling to see, and even climbing upon railings, from which they look down with faces that present a striking group, expressive of much wonder, interest, and curiosity, mixed with a little awe. And yet they look upon a spectacle which is presented in our day as a matter-of-course to thousands of young men during the winter session at the hospitals.

The woodcut at once leads us to suppose that we have to deal, in the book to which it is prefixed, with the man who was the first to force his way into a path obstructed by a heavy barricade of

* Reprinted from Henry Morley, *Clement Marot and Other Studies,* Vol. II (London, 1871), pp. 65-96.

prejudice. If we turn over a leaf, we find his portrait in another sketch, rough, bold, and masterly. It portrays spirit and flesh of a young man who has the marks of a hardworking brain upon his forehead, and of a firm will upon his face. He looks like a man born to do work for the world, and not unwilling at the same time to take ease in it. He evidently can enjoy as well as think, and will, and do. His beard is very trim, his senses look acute, his rather handsome features express much refinement, aptness also for a look of scorn. He shows like a chief in intellect, a gracious king over some region of knowledge, who possesses all he could inherit, and knows how to conquer more; a good companion to kindred minds when recognized among them as a leader. So we judge from the noble portrait of the young professor in his robes, Andrew Vesalius, aged, as we are told by the inscription on the border, twenty-eight; a man who at that age had already become the Luther of Anatomy.

We meet only occasionally with born poets and musicians. Vesalius had a native genius of a rarer kind—he was a born dissecter. From the inspection of rats, moles, dogs, cats, monkeys, his mind rose, impatient of restraint, to a desire for a more exact knowledge than they or Galen gave of the anatomy of man. But in his day, to be dissatisfied with Galen was to be a heretic in medicine; and to touch with a scalpel the dead "image of God" was reckoned impious in theology. There was no doubt left upon that latter point, for, in the lifetime of Vesalius, Charles V had brought the question formally before a consultation of divines at Salamanca. For purposes of ambition, living men might be blown asunder, at the cannon's mouth, cut up with sword and axe, or probed into with military lances. For the purposes of science, dead men were not to receive a wound.

Three weasels formed the family arms of Andreas, whose name was properly Wesalius, his forefathers having at one time belonged to Wesel, where they formed a portion of the noble Wittag family. The immediate progenitors of Andreas for several generations had been eminent for medical attainments. Peter Wesalius was a famous physician. John, the son of Peter, another thriving doctor, was physician to Mary of Burgundy, the first wife of Maximilian I. John, growing old, retired from business; not, however, until he had introduced Everard, his son, to his distinguished mistress and to all his profitable practice. Everard kept up the reputation of the family, wrote Commentaries on the books of Rhases, and upon the Aphorisms of Hippocrates. The son of Everard, and the father of Andreas, enjoyed another reputation of the same kind; he was apothecary to the Emperor. The family mind was touched by this hereditary transmission through five generations of the same pursuit. When Andreas and his brother Francisco were destined to follow the two separate professions of Medicine and Law, their father found it very difficult to keep Francisco steady to his course of jurisprudence. Sending him out to study law his father found to be like throwing a ball against a blank wall, he came regularly back upon his hand. When afterwards Francisco saw his famous brother very much attacked by Galenists, and indisposed to pay attention to them, there was nothing nearer to the heart of the young lawyer than a desire to fight his battle for him. The veins of the family, in fact, ran medicine. Andreas, when he was not fifteen years old, attended plague cases and practised surgery.

He was born on the last day of December, in the year 1514. His father, the apothecary, being attached to the service of Margaret, governor of the Netherlands, aunt of the Emperor Charles V, Andreas Vesalius was born at Brussels. He was sent as a boy to study at Louvain, where he made very rapid progress in all branches of knowledge taught to him. He manifested a great taste for science, and spent all his leisure upon practical research into the mechanism of the lower animals. He became very proficient in the scholarship of the day, so that in his great work, written before he had allowed his skill to rust, the Latin style is singularly pure. Jean Riolan, who took pains afterwards to show that Vesalius was but a shallow fellow, and that his knowledge of anatomy in particular was not much more than skin-deep, protested that he must have found some good scholar to write the Latin of his books. At the same time, however, that he might smite with a two-edged scalpel, the discerning critic blamed the sentences of Vesalius for their length and his style for its obscurity. His scalpel was blunt, for his own style was very clumsy. The good Latin written by Vesalius while he was comparatively fresh from his studies at Louvain, became corrupted by disuse. That Vesalius mastered not only Latin but Greek also, accurately, at Louvain, may be inferred from the fact that he wrote Greek annotations to the works of Galen. It is more certainly proved by the confidence with which the great Venetian printer, Aldinus Junta, in after years made application to Vesalius alone for a corrected text of Galen, and for castigation of a Latin rendering of Galen's works. The application was only in part responded to.

Greek and Latin were sources of pleasure to the young anatomist, only because they enabled him to read medical books. Then also, as he soon discovered the corruptness of translations generally, he was not content to study the Arabians by aid of their interpreters, but betook himself to a scholar learned in Arabic and Hebrew, Lazarus Hebræus de Frigeis. With that teacher he read Avicenna in the original Arabic, and afterwards was able to write for himself a paraphrase of the ten books of Rhases to the Emir Almansor.

From Louvain the youth was sent to Paris, where he studied physic under a most eminent physician, Jacobus Sylvius, otherwise Jacques de la Boë. Sylvius found his new pupil disagreeably acute. It was the practice of that illustrious professor to read to his class Galen "On the Use of Parts." He began fairly, and when he had reached the middle of the first book, at the point where the anatomy commences, he said, "Gentlemen, we now come to a part too difficult for the comprehension of beginners. Were I to go through it with you, we should only be bewildering each other." To save trouble, therefore, the professor took a flying leap over all intervening matter, and descended plump on the fifth book over which he cantered easily to the tenth section. From the rest of the work he made selections, to the consideration of which he either gave a single lecture, or to which he devoted five or six lessons at most. This course of professional study was illustrated sometimes with the dissection of some portion of a dog, prepared for the purpose by a surgeon under the professor's eye. This always was thrown away on the third day, when it became unpleasant to smell.

Sylvius believed, like his brethren, that the anatomy of all flesh was contained in Galen. If he found anything in his dog that puzzled him, the fault lay with the animal; the dog was wrong. Often the learned man—more used to turn over leaves of books than strips of muscle—blundered about his little preparation, vainly searching for some blood vessel or tendon that he meant to show. At the third of his practical demonstrations witnessed by Andreas, the teacher was so much surprised at the confused construction of the animal before him that he called upon the newcomer, whose passion for dissecting was well known, to help him through his difficulty. The professor's patience was tried farther by the fact that Andreas Vesalius, by the intensity of his own enthusiasm, infected his companions with a pitiless zeal after correct details of anatomy. Whenever Sylvius, unable to find some vein or nerve, excused its non-appearance and passed glibly on, he made work for his pupils. They slipped down when he was gone, hunted the dog through for the missing part, dissected it out for their master with great neatness, and triumphantly called his attention to it on his next appearance.

The influence of a commanding mind and of a strong enthusiasm was exercised over his associates in a yet more striking way by the ambitious student. He caused some of the young men to share his own impatience at the dog-anatomy to which they were confined. Pleasure-loving youths, moved by his impulse, were to be found with him haunting at ghostly hours the Cemetery of the Innocents. Once, when he went with a fellow-pupil to the Montfauçon, where the bodies of executed criminals were deposited and bones were plentiful, they found themselves attacked by a pack of fierce dogs. Masters of the situation, they would by no means let a bone be touched, and there ensued so hard a battle with them that Vesalius believed the dogs were at last going to get their turn as dissecters, and had agreed upon him for their first subject.

Another of the teachers under whom Andreas studied in Paris was a man of great renown, Gauthier of Andernach, or, to speak learnedly, Guintherius. He was physician in ordinary to King Francis I. Guintherius, before he went to Paris, had been Greek professor at Louvain. At Paris he occasionally ventured so far as to dissect human bodies. I run over three years to state here that in his "Institutiones Anatomicæ," published in 1536, Guinther took occasion to specify Andreas Wesalius (the classic V had not at that time been adopted in the name) as a youth of great promise, Vesalius then being twenty-one years old. Again, after three more years had elapsed, in publishing a new edition of his "Institutiones," Guinther stated that he had been indebted largely to the helping hand of Andreas Vesalius, a youth most diligent in the study of anatomy. The youth was then already himself beginning work upon a book that was to produce a revolution in the science.

At about the age of nineteen, however, the pupilage of Andreas at Paris, under Sylvius and Guinther, had been broken off by the French wars. He retired then to his alma mater at Louvain. Here, continuing his studies, he for the first time openly demonstrated from the human subject, offering to the scholars of Louvain an unaccustomed spectacle. He had himself in Paris only twice been present at a demonstration of the kind.

During his sojourn at Louvain, it happened one day that Vesalius walked with his friend Reiner (Gemma Frisius) outside the gates. Reiner, called Frisian from his birthplace, became Professor of Medicine at Louvain, and distinguished for his skill in mathematics. As a physician he was in request at the court of Charles V, but wearied of court practice and gave it up. He was noted for his short stature, and six years older than his comrade in this country walk; Vesalius twenty and he twenty-six. By accident their ramble brought them to the Tyburn of Louvain, the spot on which it was usual not only to execute criminals, but also to expose their bodies. It was a place of human bones, and of men's corpses in all stages of corruption. To such a spot the friends came very naturally, led to it no doubt by a familiar path, for where else was there a retired nook to be found of which the scenery was more completely in accordance with the taste of an anatomist? Vesalius loved nature with the ardour of true genius, but he was a man who could have boiled his kettle with more pleasure in the valley of Jehoshaphat than in the vale of Tempè. Why should he not? Is the thigh-bone that propped up a lord of the creation less to be honoured than a primrose-stalk? Or is the cup that has contained the brain and wit of man to be regarded with less tender reverence than buttercups and pumpkins?

Vesalius and Gemma Frisius, whose humour it was to admire nature in the mechanism of the human body, looked at the dead men with learned eyes. The botanist a-field looks out for specimens to carry home, so the anatomist Vesalius looked keenly about him, for in such a place the obvious question was, could he make any addition to his hortus siccus of odd joints and bones.

Now there had been executed on that spot a noted robber, who, since he deserved more than ordinary hanging, had been chained to the top of a high stake and roasted alive. He had been roasted by a slow fire made of straw, that was kept burning at some distance below his feet. In that way there had been a dish cooked for the fowls of heaven, which was regarded by them as a special dainty. The sweet flesh of the delicately roasted thief they had preferred to any other; his bones, therefore, had been elaborately picked, and there was left suspended on the stake a skeleton dissected out, and cleaned by many beaks with rare precision. The dazzling skeleton, complete and clean, was lifted up on high before the eyes of the anatomist, who had been striving hitherto to piece together such a thing out of the bones of many people, gathered as occasion offered. This was a flower to be plucked from its tall stem.

Mounting upon the shoulders of his friend, and aided by him from below, young Andreas ascended the charred stake, and tore away whatever bones he found accessible, breaking the ligaments which tied the legs and arms to the main trunk. The trunk itself was bound by iron chains so firmly to the stake, that it was left there hanging. With stolen bones under their clothes, the two young men returned to Louvain.

But in the evening Vesalius went out alone to take another walk, did not return in haste, and suffered the town gates to close against him. He had resolved to spend the night afield under the stars; while honest men were sleeping in their beds, he meant to share the vigil of the thieves. There was the trunk of the skeleton yet to be had. At midnight none would dare to brave the spectacle of fleshly horrors, to say nothing of such ghostly accidents as might befall them among corpses of the wicked, under rain, moon, stars, or flitting night clouds. Certain, therefore, that no man would come to witness his offence, Vesalius at midnight again climbed the tree to gather its remaining blossom. By main force he deliberately wrested the whole set of bones out of the grasp of the great iron fetters, and then having removed his treasure to a secret spot, he buried it. In the morning he returned home empty-handed. At leisure then, and carefully, he smuggled through the gates, day after day, bone after bone. But when the perfect skeleton was set up in his own house he did not scruple to display it openly, and to demonstrate from it, giving out that it had been brought by him to Louvain from Paris. The act of plunder was, however, too bold to escape attention. Vesalius afterwards was banished from Louvain for this offence.

In the next year, 1535, Andreas, having completed his twentieth year, served as a surgeon in the army of the Emperor Charles V, during the French war. He was then earning a salary, and finding subjects for dissection on the battle-field. Soon afterwards he went to Italy, making his head-quarters apparently at Venice, and displaying his zeal and ability as an anatomist, by demonstrating publicly under the shadow of the most famous universities. Andreas Vesalius at once excited the attention of the learned men of Italy, as a remarkable youth of twenty-one or two, who could name, with his eyes blindfolded, any, even the smallest human bone put into his hand, who was versed deeply in comparative anatomy, and had more accurate and practical knowledge of the structure of the human frame than any grey-beard of the time had dared to master. He was a youth who had turned all the ardour and passion of his age into the service of that one mysterious pursuit at which his neighbours shuddered and admired; a youth who was at the same time an able scholar, and who could declaim his knowledge in sound Latin from the lecture-table. The intensity of his zeal, and his own habit of mastery won for him in Italy so prompt a recognition of his genius, that he was only twenty-two years old when he was offered (in 1537) a professorship at Padua, created for him. It was the first purely anatomical professorship, and in accepting it Vesalius became the first Professor of Anatomy who taught the science, and received a salary for so doing from the funds of any university.

A good deal of morbid curiosity, a corrupt taste for witnessing dissections of the human body as a novel spectacle, no doubt increased the number of the new professor's hearers. He was doing a bold thing, his lectures were a striking innovation on the tameness of conventional routine, and his fame grew with proportionate rapidity. He continued to hold his professorship at Padua during seven years, but he was at the same time professor in two other universities. He was sought by the academies for the same reason that causes an attractive performer to be sought at the same time by rival managers. Wherever he appeared, the theatre would fill. When already appointed at Padua, he was endowed with a professorship also at Bologna, in which town he put together and compared the skeletons of a man and of a monkey. Being thus doubly a professor, he accepted also the urgent invitation of Cosmo, Duke of Florence, who desired that he should take office as Professor of Anatomy at Pisa. Cosmo secured his man not only by offering a salary of six hundred crowns for a short course of demonstrations, but also by commanding that the authorities should furnish him with a free supply of bodies, whether from the cemetery or the scaffold. In each university the services of the professor were confined to a short course of demonstrations, so that his duties were complete when he had spent during the winter a few weeks at each of the three towns in succession. Then he returned to Venice.

At Venice, Andreas Vesalius studied indefatigably, at the same time that he practised physic. He not only solicited the bodies of condemned criminals, but also begged of magistrates that they would sentence such men to the modes of death that he from time to time suggested, in order that he might obtain physiological knowledge from his post-mortem inspections. He was not afraid also to beg that executions might be delayed when he was well supplied with subjects, so that there might be material for him to work upon at a more leisure time. Furthermore, he watched—and incited his pupils to watch—all the symptoms in men dying of a fatal malady, and it was usual with him and them to note where, after death, such men were buried. For their bodies night visits were paid to the churchyard, either by Vesalius or by some of his pupils, and a diligent search was then made for the accurate determination of the cause of death. Many a corpse was in this way secretly conveyed by Andreas to his own chamber, and concealed in his own bed.

At Padua and Bologna, where there was no bold Cosmo to back the teacher, no public means were ventured upon for the supply of the new lecture-table. It was supplied without trouble to Vesalius by the enthusiasm of the students, who became resurrectionists on his behalf. Thus it happened that on one occasion his class was edified by the emotion of a portly Petrarch under a monk's hood, who had sought in the excitement of anatomy a refuge from his grief for the recent death of a too well-known Laura. He sat down thinking of his old acquaintance with a sigh—

> Mai non fu' in parte, ove si chiar vedessi
> Quel, che veder vorrei, poi ch'io nol vidi,—

and started with a shout that betrayed all his secret when he saw her stretched out on the demonstrator's table. She had been disinterred by the students as a friendless person—one who in life had not regarded her own flesh as sacred, and whose body, therefore, might be lectured from without risk of exciting any active outcry against desecration of the dead. Vesalius, who hated monks as false pretenders and obstructors of sound knowledge, enjoyed greatly this dilemma.

During the first three years of office as professor, Andreas did not depart, or wish to depart, from the approved rule of study. He praised the works of Galen in good faith, and made use of the anatomical writings of that ancient author as the text-book upon which he founded all his demonstrations. With practical experience, however, the conviction grew, not only that the anatomy of Galen was extremely incomplete, but that it was often wrong. He had marked down upon the margins of his text-book as he detected them many discrepancies between the text of Galen and the human body. These variations he found, as he went on, were constant. Then, dissecting lower animals, and monkeys more especially, he made comparison between their parts and corresponding parts in man, until he became convinced that Galen very rarely wrote from actual inspection of the human subject; that he had been a great anatomist, but that his teaching was based on a belief that the structure of a monkey was a direct copy of the structure of a man. Galen had not ventured often to defy superstition, and defile himself by too close contact with the dead of his own race. This fact being ascertained with certainty, Vesalius took more than usual pains to note every discrepancy between the text of Galen and the actual parts which it endeavoured to describe. The list of these variations—annotations upon Galen—formed in a short time a volume of considerable thickness.

Having thus seen reason to distrust the foundations upon which the whole structure of medical science was, in his time, built, Vesalius at the age of twenty-five resolved to reconstruct more durably the science of anatomy. He perceived only one way in which this could be done: he would dissect minutely through the human body, and write down all that he found there, carefully and accurately, in a well-digested book. He would collate upon each point the evidence obtained under the scalpel with the writings of the authorities who occupied the schools before him, would retain their nomenclature and repeat their truths, but rectify their almost countless errors. To this bold enterprise, after his genius had once admitted the idea, Vesalius was further impelled by the encouragement of his friends, and chiefly by the incitements of a colleague in the University of Padua, Mark Antony Genua, and of the patrician, Wolfgang Herwort. So it happened that, at the age of twenty-five, Andreas Vesalius, already a famous teacher, began to write, from actual scrutiny, his text-book of "The Fabric of the Human Body." He at the same time practised medicine, and expressed loudly and often his regret that the art of healing and the science of anatomy were followed as two separate pursuits. He declared a correct knowledge of anatomy to be essential both to the physician and the surgeon, and he taught the science in his writings with a constant reference to medicine and surgery, bitterly ridiculing those practitioners who got their knowledge of disease out of a study of syrups.

It is possible to tell in a few paragraphs all that is known to have been done before the time of Vesalius for the promotion of the study of true human anatomy. In very ancient times it is proved that there was no lack of dissectors, those of the Alexandrian school used the knife freely on the human subject. Herophilus is said to have cut up and examined three hundred bodies without reckoning his vivisections. Of the anatomy of the ancients, however, nothing has been transmitted except what has come down to us in the extant works of Galen. Galen, it has been shown, dissected lower animals and monkeys—rarely man. When contact with a corpse made expiations and ablutions necessary, it was not an easy thing to be an accurate anatomist. After the death of Galen that chief still continued to hold sway for centuries over the world of medicine. The Arabians put implicit faith in him, and copied all his errors, adding many of their own.

In the middle ages practical anatomy when it attempted any inspection of "the Divine image" was regarded as impiety; nevertheless, a first step in a right direction was made by Mondino, about the year 1315. Mondino, professor of medicine at Bologna, between the years 1315-18, exhibited the public dissection of three bodies, and by so doing was the cause of a great scandal. Alarmed by an edict of Pope Boniface VII he gave up his dangerous experiment, but he had published a work "On Anatomy," containing much original matter, which was adopted by the learned world, and prescribed to be read in all academies.

For three centuries this work continued to be in force as an authority. In the time of Vesalius, Mondino was read commonly as a supplement to the anatomy contained in Galen, and if any anatomist had new facts to record, he edited Mondino, and attached to the text of that author his own experience in the form of commentary. In the year 1520, Mondino had in that way been supplied with notes by Alessandro Achillini, and edited by his poet-brother Philothes, at Bologna; and in 1521 the book of Mondino was again amply illustrated by Jacques Berenger, the best of the precursors of Vesalius. Mondino wrote succinctly, treating of parts in their natural order, but his information was not only succinct but also meagre; his style being obscure and barbarous, often incomprehensible, his errors many. His errors were so many that Matteo Corti—who spoke before Vesalius had shaken the old paramount authority—said of Mondino "all that is right in him is Galen's, but his own matter is always wrong." Achillini was pronounced jejune, Berenger diffuse, but really good. Jacques Berenger introduced also into his edition, for the first time, pictures, by which the eye was enabled to comprehend the details given in the letter-press. The pictures were rude, nineteen in number, increased in another publication, two years afterwards, to twenty-two. These plates deserve to be remembered by anatomists as the first efforts that were made to facilitate their studies by depicting as well as describing the human frame. In 1534, Albert Durer depicted the symmetry of the human body in four books, but rather as an artist than as an anatomist. The greatest painters, protected by Julius II and Leo X, had been allowed to study practically just so much anatomy as was required for the perfection of their art. Drawings from nature of the superficial muscles had been made by Leonardo da Vinci, Raffaelle, and Michael Angelo. Representations of the anatomy of deep-seated parts immediately preceding the publication of the plates issued by Vesalius, were edited in 1540 by Walter Hermann Ryff; and a more valuable set, in which the brain is well depicted with its parts figured and named, was published by Balthasar Becker. None of these works were at all calculated to disturb the supremacy of Galen, or to create any revolution in anatomy. But they were indications of the ripeness of the field for work like that to which Vesalius devoted himself with the whole fresh zeal of youth and all the vigour of his genius.

The income derived by Andreas from three professorships, and from his practice among the Venetians, perhaps also the prosperous worldly condition of his family, enabled him to spend money freely in the prosecution of his literary work. He took pains to secure, not only for his description of parts, but also for the representations of them to be published in his book, the utmost possible fidelity and beauty. It cost him not a little to tempt able artists from their studies of the beautiful to sit and paint, day after day, from a dissected corpse. Grudging no cost, he succeeded so well as to obtain for his book anatomical plates not only incomparably better than any that had been previously published, but more excellent as works of art than very many that have appeared since his day. The chief artist engaged with him in this labour was Johann Stephan von Calcar, native of Calcar, in the duchy of Cleves. That artist studied during his best years in Italy, admiring chiefly the works of Raffaelle and Titian. He was one of the most able of Titian's pupils, and so accurately seized his master's style and manner, that many works from the hands of Calcar, portraits especially, have been attributed to Titian. Rubens kept, until his death, a Nativity by Calcar, that was remarkable for its effects of light; and Calcar is well known to many in our own day as the painter of the portraits which accompany Vasari's Lives; Calcar, then, was the chief artist engaged upon the anatomical figures published by Vesalius, and so it happened that those figures were in their own time often attributed to Titian.

While Andreas was steadily at work upon his book, author and artists (another artist was Nicholas Stoop) making simultaneous progress, the first few plates were sent to the professor's father, who, it may be remembered, was apothecary to the Emperor. By him they were shown to Charles V, also to many of his most distinguished courtiers, and in this way the praise of the young anatomist first came to be spoken from imperial lips. In the year 1539, at the age of twenty-five, Vesalius issued to the public a few completed plates as an experiment. Being successful in Italy, they were largely pirated by German publishers, and many bad copies of these plates are therefore extant. The Opus Magnum was again to be preceded by another herald, an epitome of its six books with illustrations of the choicest kind. In this epitome the matter was arranged and the plates were chosen with a direct intent to supply that kind of information wanted commonly by surgeons. The chief care of the book was to describe and depict accurately those parts which are most frequently exposed to wounds, dislocations, tumours, and such ills of the flesh. It was to serve also as an index to the greater work. Although the epitome was finished first, and dedicated in due form to Philip, son and heir of the great Emperor, the actual publication of it was delayed until some months after the appearance of the full and perfect work, the "Corporis Humani Fabrica," first published at Basle, in the year 1543, its author being at that time twenty-eight years old.

With the famous treatise of Vesalius upon the "Fabric of the Human Body" begins the history of anatomy as it is now studied. In that book the plates are throughout to the letter-press what the real subject is to the lecture of the demonstrator, and the references to the pictures are minute, distinct, and accurate. The groundwork of true human anatomy is laid, throughout the book, with an exactness never before approached. The work is strictly anatomical, but it includes many important references to the allied subjects of physiology and surgery. The descriptions of parts are given in well-polished Latin, with the clearness of a man who is quite master of his subject, and, as he goes on, the author makes a merciless comparison between the structure that is really found in man and the description of it found in Galen. He shows, finally, by cumulative proof, that Galen taught from a knowledge, not of men, but of brutes. Because, in showing this, Vesalius proved errors not only of Galen, but of the whole mass of his brethren—who had gone to Galen only for their information, and whom he would compel to sit at his own feet for better knowledge—he knew well that he was provoking all the brotherhood to war. He therefore made his onslaught upon error in a fighting mood.

Old men were not willing to tolerate dictation from a boy of twenty-eight. Professors and physicians who maintained a reputation for wisdom in their universities and in the world by propping it upon an intimate acquaintance with the works of Galen were not disposed to let their prop be struck away; they held to it tenaciously. Sylvius at Paris was especially indignant at the scientific heresies of his late pupil; he attacked his book with violence. Vesalius, therefore, wrote to his old master a letter full of friendly feeling and respect, inquiring wherein he had been guilty of error. Sylvius replied to this that he liked his old pupil very well, and would be glad to call him friend, but he could do so only on condition that he would show proper respect to Galen. If he failed in that, he was to expect no quarter either from Sylvius or any pupils of his school.

Soon after the publication of his work in 1543, the name of Andreas Vesalius had become widely known at Court as that of a man gifted with preternatural skill in the art of healing. In the year 1546 Andreas went from Venice, then his home, in company with the Venetian ambassador, to Regensburg, where he was to exercise his skill upon the Emperor, and from that date he was ranked among the Emperor's physicians. On his way to Regensburg, he stopped for a short time at Basle, and there gave a few demonstrations from a skeleton prepared by himself, which, upon leaving, he presented to the University. The skeleton was hung up in the lecture-hall with an inscription under it commemorating the event, and it is still one of the curiosities of Basle.

From the Emperor, Vesalius was sent in the same year to attend one of his nobles. Afterwards at Ratisbon he wrote and published (still in 1546) one of his works, a long letter to Joachim Roelants, on the use of China-root (one of the sarsaparillas). In that work, while he professed to treat of the medicine by which the Emperor's health had been restored, he entered largely into a vindication of his teaching against all assailants, and a fresh exposition of the fact that Galen had dissected brutes alone. The letter, of which the greater part was devoted to the business of self-assertion, contains much autobiographic matter, and is the source from which many of the preceding details have been drawn.

Returning then to Italy—his age being thirty-two—Andreas again taught and dissected publicly at Bologna, Padua, and Pisa. His object was to battle against opposition from the orthodox. With few exceptions all the young men—all the next generation of physicians—declared themselves enthusiastically to be of the party of Vesalius. The old scholars and practitioners declared that innovator to be a mere infidel in anatomy, teaching a mass of errors. Vesalius, to put down these people, wrote always on the day before each of his demonstrations a public notice that it would take place, and that all men who decried his errors were invited to attend to make their own dissections from his subject, and confound him openly. Not a man ventured to accept the challenge, and in this way the opposition to Vesalius on the part of his immediate neighbours was held very much in check.

But from the old-fashioned teachers of the young in other towns —especially from Sylvius in Paris—the outcry against the heretic who had endeavoured to shake faith in the word of Galen was incessant. In the year 1551 Sylvius broke out in print; his wrath was a long madness, and in his published lucubration the display of it runs to an excess that is pitiable. He accuses his old pupil, whom, by way of a dull, rude joke, he everywhere calls Vesanus, as a monster of ignorance, arrogance, and ingratitude—a man who poisoned

Europe by the breath of his impiety, and who clouded knowledge
by the infinitude of all his blunders. The animosity of Sylvius had
become bitterly personal, and he even went so far as to accuse Andreas to the Emperor, and to seek an ally in one of the imperial
physicians, Cornelius Barsdrop, whom he endeavoured to bribe,
not with money but with bones, namely, the skeleton of a child.
All this hatred was not spent in vain. Sylvius was called upon, as
a credible witness, to substantiate his charges, by exhibiting the
errors of Vesalius from his own dissection of the subject. He was
unable to do so. The human body was perverse, and followed the
descriptions of the heretic; but so completely was belief in Galen
the religion of the old physicians, that Sylvius next declared the
men of his own time to be constructed somewhat differently from
the men who had lived so many centuries before. The ancients, at
any rate, it was quite certain that Galen had dissected and described
infallibly. Rather let him believe that God's work had been altered
than that Galen had confounded men with monkeys.

The outcry raised against him by so many grave authorities did,
in effect, create in many minds a vague dread of Vesalius and his
writings. They fell into bad odour at Court; he performed wonderful
cures, but when so much testimony went to show that the young
man's writing was arrogant and impious, it was felt that it must
be wrong to countenance his books. When, therefore, for the sake
of his reputed skill as a practitioner of medicine, Vesalius was
called to reside permanently at Madrid, the summons was attended
with so many circumstances showing the success of those who
clamoured at his writings, that in a fit of proud indignation he
spent one unlucky hour in burning all his manuscripts. Thus he
destroyed a huge volume of annotations upon Galen; a whole book
of Medical Formulæ; many original notes upon drugs; the copy
of Galen from which he lectured, covered with marginal notes of
new observations that had occurred to him while demonstrating;
and the paraphrase of the books of Rhases, in which the knowledge
of the Arabians was collated with that of the Greeks and others.
The produce of the labour of many years was thus destroyed in

a short fit of passion. While the ashes of his manuscripts were yet before him, Andreas repented of his deed.

He lived no more for science. As a Court Physician at Madrid it was of no use for Vesalius to teach anatomy to the church from bodies robbed out of the consecrated ground. He lived upon his reputation, and indulged in all the ease compatible with the stiff life of a Spanish courtier. There was a second (augmented) edition of his "Fabric of the Human Body," published at Basle in 1555; but it was left for scholars and physicians to fight out among themselves the question of its merits. Vesalius was dead to controversy and to study, but alive to gain and pleasure.

The reputation he enjoyed as a physician was unbounded. One instance of his wonderful sagacity is an instructive example of the growth of knowledge among men of the lancet. There is now scarcely one hospital pupil in his third year who would not be ashamed to fail in the diagnosis of an aneurismal tumour. Such a tumour on a patient—a big and wonderful tumour on the loins— puzzled two famous imperial physicians, Adolf Oceone and Achilles Piriminus. Vesalius being called into consultation, said: "There is a blood vessel dilated; that tumour is full of blood." They were surprised at so strange an opinion; but the man died, the tumour was opened, blood was actually found in it, and all were in a rapture of astonishment.

Another case was of a more startling kind, though not so creditable to the wit of the physician. In 1548 Maximilian d'Egmont, Count of Buren, a favourite general, was ill at Brussels. He had a disease of the heart, and Vesalius being called in not only said that he would die, but undertook also to predict the day and hour of death. In those days of astrology and superstition the habit of desiring and of hazarding predictions was extremely common. Vesalius had seldom risked his reputation by the use of them; but this one (as I hope he did not feel that it would do) brought its own fulfilment. The dread anticipation occupied the Count's mind. On the appointed day he called his relatives and friends together to a feast, distributed gifts, declared his last wishes, took formal leave of all, waited with strong suppressed emotion for the appointed hour of death, and at the hour predicted actually died.

After the abdication of Charles V, Vesalius remained attached to the Court of Philip II. Don Carlos, Philip's son, in chasing a girl of the palace who fled from him, fell down a flight of stairs and so received a very severe blow on his head. There was great swelling and the Prince lay hopelessly insensible until Vesalius, fetched from a distance, cut into the scalp and relieved his patient promptly.

Brother physicians, however, said even at Court that Vesalius understood only superficial injuries, and could not cure internal disease. Vesalius replied easily that the world outside the profession had a different opinion, and that he had no reason to envy any doctor in the world the income he could make out of his skill. When Henry II of France was lying mortally sick of his lance-wound, it was Vesalius whom Philip of Spain sent to save him from the clutch of death. But it was a long way from Madrid, and death was travelling much faster than the doctor.

The controversy concerning the infallibility of Galen was, in the meantime, raging with considerable violence. Renatus Henerus, a young man studying at Paris under Sylvius, felt annoyed at the incessant outcry against Vesalius with which that professor was continually worrying his classes. He heard also that many sound and mature men disapproved of what, to his fresh heart, appeared very much like the bitterness of bigotry. Fuchs at Tübingen, Massa at Venice, and Rondolet at Montpellier, first-rate authorities, taught already without scruple many things that contradicted Galen. Henerus, finding this to be the case, determined on his own part to speak out on behalf of the too-much abused reformer. He published, therefore, at Venice, in 1554, an apology for Vesalius, in which he spoke of Sylvius always with the respect due from a pupil to his teacher, and declared that he had never seen the man whose reputation he defended. Among other attacks upon the great anatomist was one published in 1562 by Francisco Puteo of Vercelli; but at that time Vesalius had shaken off a little of his lethargy, being apparently impressed with the belief that his fame was not secure. There appeared, therefore, a sharp reply to Puteo from a writer calling himself Gabriel Cuneus. That writer Jerome Cardan, his contemporary and friend, with the best opportunities of knowing the truth, identifies with Andreas Vesalius himself. Internal evidence corroborates the statement of Cardan.

The fears of Vesalius concerning his good fame in the world of science had been excited in the year 1561, by the appearance of the "Anatomical Observations" of Falloppio. Giovanni Bonacci, whose pseudonym was Gabriel Falloppio, had been one of his pupils, and having mastered all the knowledge of his chief, had continued, with great skill and industry, to push forward the knowledge of anatomy. While the scalpel of Vesalius was rusting, Falloppio was making new researches; and when, in the year 1561, he published the results of his labours, after thirteen years of public teaching in Ferrara, and after having presided for eight years over an anatomical school, he was, of course, able to enlarge the borders of the science. With a temper that more suited the tone of feeling in a courtier than in a scholar, Vesalius regarded the advanced knowledge of his pupil as an infringement of his rights. Though he had been twenty years away from work as an anatomist, and had at that time in Madrid no opportunity of testing the discoveries of Falloppio by actual dissection, he wrote hastily an angry, wrongheaded reply, an "Examination of the Observations of Falloppio," in which he decried the friend who made improvements on himself, as he had been himself decried for his improvements upon Galen. The manuscript of this work, finished at the end of December, in the year 1561, Andreas committed to the care of Paolo Tiepolo, of Venice, orator to the King of Spain, who was to give it to Falloppio. War, however, so far obstructed traveling, that the orator did not reach Padua until after the death of Falloppio; he then very wisely retained and kept to himself all knowledge of the MS. Vesalius soon afterwards, on his way to Jerusalem, took possession of his work and caused it to be published without more delay. It appeared, therefore, at Venice in the year 1564.

The journey to Jerusalem, on which Vesalius set out from Madrid when in the full noon of his prosperity, is thus accounted for in a letter from Hubert Languet, Sir Philip Sidney's old Huguenot friend, to Caspar Teucher: "Vesalius, believing a young Spanish nobleman, whom he had attended, to be dead, obtained from his parents leave to open him, for the sake of inquiring into the real cause of his illness, which he had not rightly comprehended. This was granted; but he had no sooner made a cut into the body than he perceived symptoms of life, and, opening the breast, saw the heart beat. The parents coming afterwards to know of this, were not satisfied with prosecuting him for murder, but accused him of impiety to the Inquisition, in the hope that he would be punished with greater rigour by the judges of that tribunal than by those of the common law. But the King of Spain interfered and saved him, on condition, however, that by way of atonement he should make a pilgrimage to the Holy Land."

Boerhaave and Albinus, in the notice of Vesalius prefixed to their edition of his works, observe that the heart cannot well beat with life after so much dissection of the human frame as is necessary to expose it to the eye. It has been known, however, for centuries, that the irritability of muscles continues after death, differing in different parts, and may be excited mechanically by slight stimulus. The ventricles of the heart lose the contractile power within fifty minutes after death; but in the auricles it remains for hours—longer, indeed, than in any other muscle. Such facts had been observed even by Galen, who, perceiving that in the right auricle the power of contracting under stimulus remained longer than in any other portion of the body, described that part as the *ultimum moriens*—the last to die. Involuntary contraction of this kind may have helped in the ruin of Vesalius, or perhaps the priests, who had long watched their opportunity, took care to make the most of a mechanical gurgling in the body, or a chance movement occasioned by some shaking of the table, and contrived at last so to fix with a fatal weight the accusation of impiety upon the bold man who had so long set them at defiance.

Quitting Madrid for Venice, Andreas set out upon the next stage of his journey; from Venice to Cyprus, in company with Giacomo Malatesta di Rimini, General of the Venetian army. From Cyprus he went on to Jerusalem, and was returning, not to Madrid, but to the labours of his youth as a Professor at Padua, being invited by the Venetian Senate to occupy the Chair of Physic in that University, vacant by the death of Falloppio, when he was shipwrecked in the neighborhood of Zante. Cast ashore upon that island, there he perished miserably, of hunger and grief, on the 15th of October of the year 1564, before he had quite reached the age of fifty. His body was found some days afterwards, in a miserable hut, by a travelling goldsmith, who recognised in its starved outlines the features of the renowned Andreas Vesalius.

At the goldsmith's cost, therefore, the shipwrecked man was buried among strangers. After his death a great work on surgery appeared, in seven books, signed with his name, and commonly included among his writings. There is reason, however, to believe that his name was stolen to give value to the book, which was compiled and published by a Venetian, Prosper Bogarucci, a literary crow, who fed himself upon the dead man's reputation.

# CONRAD GESNER*

What I shall relate here of the life of Conrad Gesner, of Zurich, will be drawn chiefly from a memoir published very soon after his death, and written by a brother student and companion, Josiah Simler. The memoir is simple and unaffected: it contains no syllable of panegyric, but leaves the facts of Gesner's life to speak in their own language to the hearts of scholars. It is dedicated to Caspar Wolff and George Kellner; two other friends of Gesner, one of whom, Wolff, succeeded to the naturalist's books and papers. Josiah Simler, in the dedication, speaks with true Swiss simplicity, and with a graceful tenderness as well, about his little record of their old companion: "It seemed to me that I owed this duty to a most dear friend, whom while he lived I greatly loved and sought, and by whom I felt my love to be returned."

Conrad Gesner, born at Zurich in the year 1516, was the son of a worker in hides. His father's Christian name was Ursus, and his mother's Barbara; but they were in name only barbarous or bearish. They were poor, for they had many children; but they lived honestly, and behaved as members of a civilised Swiss town. Conrad was

* Reprinted from Henry Morley, *Clement Marot and Other Studies,* Vol. II (London, 1871), pp. 97-131.

sent by them, while very young, to the town school, where he studied the rudiments of Greek and Latin, under very competent teachers, namely, Thomas Plattner, who removed afterwards to Basle, Theodore Buchman, Oswald Geishäuser, and Peter Rauchfuss. Buchman expounded Scripture in Zurich; Geishhäuser afterwards had charge of the church in Basle; Rauchfuss excelled in Greek, and became Greek Professor in the then very celebrated school of Strasburg.

Gesner, even from the tenderest years of his childhood, showed a studious character, and a great power of retaining knowledge. His father was too poor to pay on his account for more than the first years of wholesome necessary education. Happily, a teacher in the college, John Jacob Ammian, Professor of Latin and Oratory, saw in Conrad so much promise for the future, that he took the young scholar into his house and instructed him gratuitously for three years, believing, with a noble patriotism, that whatever labour he might spend upon the boy would be repaid in a few years to Zurich. Conrad Gesner thus became enabled to attend, not only the lectures of Ammian upon Latin and oratory, but also those of the Professor of Greek, Rodolf Collin, a peasant's son, who was interpreting Plutarch. While the youth was in this way fully occupied, and had delivered up his whole mind to dialectics, oratory, and Greek, civil war had broken out, and his father, the leatherseller, being among those who went out to fight, was not among those who came home again. He was killed in the battle of Zug, in the year 1531.

Conrad was then fifteen years old, and lay in his mother's house seriously ill. On his recovery it became necessary that he should not remain a burden on the widow, for she had other children to support, with means that had become more contracted since her husband's death. The student-son went, therefore, to Strasburg, and attached himself for some months to the service of a celebrated Lutheran, Wolfgang Fabricius Capito. Possibly his old master, Rauchfuss, had helped him to this situation, in which he enlarged his opportunities of study, and acquired a fair knowledge of Hebrew

—a language of which he already had picked up the rudiments at home.

Meanwhile, the generous John Jacob Ammian and his other learned friends in Zurich had not forgotten the young Conrad Gesner. After a brief stay in Strasburg, Conrad returned to his native town, to be sent out, with a stipend, by the scholastic senate of Zurich, on an educational mission into France. Johann Fricius went with him—a fellow-student, bound to him in those days by parity of disposition and community of study, who through manhood remained afterwards one of his warmest friends. They went to Bourges, where Gesner, then only sixteen years old, acted for twelve months as a teacher, communicating what he knew to others, and in all spare time reading for himself, incessantly, Latin and Greek, to perfect his acquaintance with those languages. Having spent a year in this way, Conrad went to Paris, being attracted thither by the University. In Paris he found many famous men, and listened to much teaching; but he was accustomed to say afterwards that he learned little at Paris, for want of counsel in the regulation of his studies. Gesner stands pre-eminent among all scholars as a wonderful economist of time. It is doubtful whether in his whole life, from the first school-days to the moment of death, he suffered as many hours and minutes as would make, when summed up, one day to be wasted. And even though his industry was so incessant, it would still be manifestly impossible that he could have left behind, after a short life, such works as now remain to us, unless he had not only worked incessantly, but understood most thoroughly the art of working at all times in the right way. This art, in the warm days of his youth, Gesner had not acquired. At Paris, he used to say, he had no regularity in study. He revelled luxuriously (he was seventeen years old) among the Greeks and Latins, equally ready to delight in poets, orators, historians, physicians, or philologists. In his youthful audacity he thought that his mind had capacity to hold them all, and this habit of gluttonous reading weakened his mind, he said, by leading him into the vice of skipping. He read over his books, not through them. Readers of to-day will not judge sternly this one blot upon the early life of Conrad Gesner.

The industry of Gesner, however, was not confined wholly to the world of books; even in those days his hours of travel and of out-door exercise were periods of active study. There was a pure-hearted Swiss pastor, Johann Fricius by name, who devoted all his leisure to botanical pursuits; this pastor, who was Conrad's uncle, conceived early a great affection for his clever nephew, and had delighted to take the child with him among the mountains, on plant-gathering excursions. Then he would expound as he could to his apt scholar the mysteries of nature, and watch the glow of the boy's pleasure in them. The impression made on Gesner's fresh heart by association with the herb-loving pastor, Fricius, strength-ened with time; and herborising never ceased throughout his after life to be the scholar's chief delight. On the way to Bourges, at Bourges, on the way from Bourges to Paris, around Paris, and along the homeward road, Gesner diligently spent his out-door time in the collection of every plant new to his eyes, and in com-paring what he found, whenever it was possible, with the descrip-tions of plants given by Dioscorides and other ancient authors. I wish to believe that Johann Fricius, who was young Gesner's com-panion and bosom friend in that journey through part of France, and afterwards in the whole journey through life, who was bound to him by similarity of tastes, and at whose side Conrad afterwards was buried by his fellow-citizens, must have been a son of the good pastor, Johann Fricius. It is very natural to think that in the dwell-ing of the pastor, or while trotting about [with] him upon the mountains, Gesner and Fricius acquired those common tastes by which they were to the last united.

From Paris Gesner returned to Strasburg, in which town he had made friends from whom he hoped to get increase of knowledge. Being summoned back to Zurich by the scholastic senate, in whose service he was engaged, the youth, who was not then quite twenty years old, earned his stipend as a teacher in the school wherein he had himself received the rudiments of classical instruction. At this period, says Josiah Simler, evidently concerned about what he thought a very weak point in the young scholar's character—*nescio quo consilio, uxorem tempestivius duxit*. One of the prevailing features in the life of Conrad Gesner, scarcely second to his marvellous assiduity in study, was his gentleness of heart, his spirit of kindly courtesy, the suavity of temper for which men of letters ought to be, but are not at all times, distinguished. He was always apt at loving, and though he was at no time guilty of any worldly folly or excess, he did not cumber his mind much with worldly wisdom. Therefore Gesner married a true-hearted girl when he was not quite twenty years of age, and had no wealth beyond the stipend of assistant-teacher and the available resources of a very well-filled head.

In school, the young husband taught to the boys rudiments of Greek and Latin grammar. At home he worked at the books of the physicians. Still he prosecuted his researches in the fields, allying botany readily enough to a course of medical reading, since in that day plants were studied chiefly with reference to any use that they might have as remedies. Gesner proposed to himself the attainment of the dignity of a physician, which if it did not—in Zurich, at any rate—obtain for him much money as a healer of disease, would give him standing in the learned world, and enable him to rise, from the stool of a teacher of rudiments, to the chair of a professor in his native town. Still receiving from the scholastic senate the same stipend paid to him at home, Gesner was sent to Basle, where he continued his study of medicine, and was assiduous in labour for a perfect acquirement of the Greek language, in which the best medical learning of the ancients—whose science the moderns followed carefully in Gesner's days—was written.

Designing at the same time to increase and strengthen his familiarity with Greek, and to provide, if possible, increased means in support of the little home he had erected, Gesner at this period of his life undertook to revise and enlarge a Greek and Latin lexicon which had been already issued, very badly done, by persons who did not put their names upon the title page. Over this task the young student took much pains, and he delivered to the printer not only the old lexicon, with its mistakes corrected, but a large body of additions drawn from the Greek Thesaurus of Guarini, otherwise Varinus, of Favera near Camerino. The printer, however, without Gesner's knowledge, used only a small part of those additions, reserving, probably, the rest to give increased attraction to another issue. Soon afterwards, by the printer's death, whatever plan he had was superseded; but Gesner's papers, over which the student had spent many days of toil, could never be recovered. Afterwards Gesner was employed three or four times by Henry Peter, bookseller, of Basle, in the further amendment and increase of this dictionary, with the addition of authorities from his own reading.

When he had spent about a year at Basle, and become exceedingly well versed in Greek, the senate of Berne having founded a new university at Lausanne, and offered liberal stipends for professors, Gesner obtained a professorship, and went to Lausanne. There he remained for three years as professor of Greek, and acquired the warm friendship of Peter Viret, and Beatus Comes, minister of the church, of Himbert, the professor of Hebrew, and Johann Rebitt, who succeeded Gesner in his chair. The friendship of these men abided with him to the end of his career. Being thoroughly familiar with the subject of his public teaching, Gesner required to spend no time in preparation for his duties in the university, he had therefore a good deal of leisure during those three years at Lausanne, which he was entitled to fill up with his own pursuits. He studied medicine still, and as he had edited lexicons while getting up his Greek, so now he issued a few medical books, which were in part original, in part epitomes and compilations, and in part translations from the Greek physicians. Pursuing still, while at Lausanne, his botanical studies, he published also a "Catalogue of Plants," in the alphabetical order of their Latin names; their names in Greek, German, and French being in each case added. In the compilation of this Catalogue, he followed Jean de la Ruelle, Leonard Fuchs, and Jerome Böck (Hieronymus Tragus); not, however, without occasionally differing from their statements, or adding new observations that belonged entirely to himself. During the same period, Gesner published also a short "History of Plants." In this history, the descriptions of plants were drawn from Dioscorides, the omissions of Dioscorides being supplied from Theophrastus, Pliny, or more modern Greeks; the properties were added in paragraphs condensed from Paulus Ægineta, Galen, or Ælian. During this period of study at Lausanne, Gesner also published a book on the "Preparation and Selection of Simple Medicaments." During the same period he published also a compendium of Galen's book upon the composition of medicaments, arranged according to genera, and according to the parts of the body upon which their healing virtue operated, beginning at the head and ending at the heel, with a collection of precepts. He issued during these three years other books also, containing the essence of his voluminous readings among Greek physicians, and also some fruits of his study of Greek for its own sake—volumes becoming his position as a Greek professor, such as an "Essay on the Wanderings of Ulysses," and what Homer meant to represent by them. As Gesner in the course of a short life issued seventy-two works from the press, besides leaving at his death eighteen that were unfinished but in progress, it is obviously impossible to give in a few pages even a brief account of all his writings. In this notice of his life it must suffice, therefore, to name occasionally a few minor works, by way of indicating the direction taken by his industry, and to attempt a description only of the most important products of his labour.

After three years spent at Lausanne, publicly as a professor of Greek, privately as a student of medicine, Conrad Gesner went—botanizing, of course, by the way—to Montpellier, of which place the medical school was famous throughout France. His design in going to Montpellier was to obtain admission as a resident for some months in the house of any distinguished physician, for he believed that by watching the domestic life and daily practice of such a man, by familiar speech with him, and in the daily intercourse of friendship, he might perfect his knowledge in a short time, more thoroughly than by attendance at the public lectures. Public teaching demonstrated, for the most part, only those doctrines of the ancients which Gesner in his own house had already mastered. At Montpellier, however, he found none of the more eminent physicians able to receive him as a house pupil; he therefore stayed but a short time in attendance on the lectures of the celebrated men through whom Montpellier was famous, and then returned to Switzerland, prepared to take his medical degree. At Basle, having heard the teaching of the principal physicians, being instructed chiefly by Albane Thorer and Sebastian Singeler, he held the usual disputations, was formally admitted to the dignity of doctor, and withdrew to settle in his native town. He was then twenty-five years old.

The first half of Gesner's life was then completed, for he died before he reached the age of fifty. He had spent twenty-five years in the incessant toil of preparation for a worthy place among his fellow-townsmen; he then settled in Zurich, and began amply to fulfill the expectations of his old friend Ammian, and of the scholastic senate of the town. In a very short time he received the appointment of Professor of Philosophy, which he retained until his death, when his friends Caspar Wolff and George Kellner succeeded him. At the same time he practised medicine, and published from time to time the fruits, as will be seen presently, of an almost incredible amount of study. During the twenty-four years of his mature life in Zurich, Gesner's wife was always his companion. He had no children of his own, but in his later years a sister with her children became dependent upon his ungrudging aid, and probably formed part of his domestic circle.

Conrad Gesner had a very great pleasure in the study of languages; he not only understood many, and read the books of many nations, but he studied language for its own sake, and, as usual, testified the thoroughness of his investigations by the books to which they led. Already, at the age of twenty-five, he was acquainted intimately with half-a-dozen tongues, Hebrew, Greek, Latin, German, Italian, and French, and he had been only three years settled in Zurich when he published his first great work, the "Universal Dictionary," a piece of bibliography which it is very hard to believe the work of a man only twenty-nine years old. It is an alphabetical catalogue—wonderfully full—of authors famous or obscure, ancient or modern, with a statement of what they had written and the argument of their books, drawn in very many cases from the prefaces inserted in the books themselves. This Dictionary was first published in the year 1545. Three years afterwards it was followed by a companion volume, entitled "Nineteen Books of the Pandects." It contains the matter of the Dictionary grouped into subjects. Thus, one book contains an alphabetical catalogue of existing works on grammar and philology, another contains the bibliography of dialectics, rhetoric, astrology, geography, or jurisprudence, and so forth.

The twentieth book, containing authors who had written upon medicine, was omitted as imperfect; but in the following year the twenty-first book of the Pandects was issued separately, containing the writers upon Christian theology. As an index to authors who wrote before the year 1545, Gesner's "Universal Dictionary" and "Pandects" remain to this day very valuable.

These volumes were the result of immense study, though it will presently be seen that they were trifles in comparison with the whole body of Gesner's work. During the toil of labours as a naturalist in the study and the field, Gesner continued to amuse himself with philological researches, and in order to complete our view of his industry in this direction, I may mention here the publication, in the year 1555, when he was thirty-nine years old, of his "Mithridates," on different languages, ancient and modern. To German, his own language, he devoted more especial study. When, in his publications as a naturalist, he described birds, beasts, or fishes hitherto unknown, or known only to the learned by the names of science, he invented names for them adapted to the genius of his mother tongue, and so endeavoured to enable all his countrymen to talk familiarly about them. If all scientific men who have lived since his day had followed his example, it would not be so difficult as it now is to diffuse a taste for science. But what ordinary man will dare to seek an exact knowledge of science when there is an army of barbarous terms defending every approach to it. However much a man may love plants, will he study them minutely when they are to be wedged into his memory under such names as escholzia, krynitskia, gleditschia? Gesner, then, so far as his own study went, endeavoured to give to every object in nature, that was not already supplied with one, a household name in his own language. He also published a list of German proper names that had been made out and sent to him by some curious friend, appending his own annotations and discussions on their etymology; and he was still busily studying German etymologies (among a great number of other things) when death bade him put his books aside. Greek, Gesner worked at as the language in which all the best materials of study were contained. For this reason it was among languages, next to German, the subject of his most assiduous attention, and he became little less familiar with it than with the tongue in which his wife addressed him. He studied with an intense thoroughness not only the Greek physicians and philosophers, but also the grammarians, theologians, orators, and poets. Whenever in his reading he encountered a new fact, either adding to his knowledge in philosophy or illustrating in some apt way a nice point in the structure of the language, it was retained in his mind, and always afterwards was to be found when wanted. Enough has been already said to make it obvious that Gesner was aided in his studies by an extraordinary memory. The student, it should be said, not only read Greek but wrote Greek, his lightest relaxation was the composition of Greek idyls, and he would write Greek letters to a learned friend, breaking occasionally out of prose into facile iambics. He translated Greek authors, amended the text of Aristotle, Theophrastus, Dioscorides, Oppian, and others. He also spoke fluently in Greek, which had become a second mother tongue to him, and in that language expounded Greek philosophy occasionally to the more advanced students of his class.

Gesner studied in all branches of the philosophy known to his own time, but chiefly physics, as the branch most nearly allied to medicine. Physics and ethics were the subjects of his professorial teaching during the twenty-four years of his mature life at Zurich. Sometimes he taught directly from the Nicomachean ethics and the physics of Aristotle, but more frequently he suited his prelections to the capacity of younger hearers, and made use in his class of the compendiums of Melanchthon (not to say Schwartzerde), Schegke, Wildenberg, Sebastian Fuchs, and others.

The natural objects in the study of which Gesner felt the greatest interest were plants, animals, and metals; these he regarded as objects offering more distinct ground for inquiry than such intangible matters as meteors, &c., and he believed also that from a study of these, useful knowledge could more readily be drawn for the advantage of medicine and the arts of life. In studying these subjects with a direct reference to their practical importance, it was Gesner's determination to collect, and if possible discover, facts, but not to theorise. By far the greatest of his literary works was the "History of Animals," and he undertook to devote his chief labour rather to animals than to plants, because of plants many had written; and on metals, a work had been published in his own time by George Bauer: concerning animals, however, little had been said.

Gesner's "History of Animals" was commenced very soon after his final settlement in Zurich, and the first book was published in the year 1549, Gesner then being thirty-three years old. For the preparation of this history Gesner undertook a course of reading in all previous authors who had touched upon his subject in any way, compared them, and selected whatever he thought best from Greeks, Latins, and Barbarians, ancients and moderns, writers famous and obscure. He undertook also what journeys he could afford in search of animals and plants. He visited some parts of Italy, and spent a month in Venice, for the purpose of examining and sketching fishes of the Mediterranean. He visited also various parts of Germany, and was about to descend the Rhine to the ocean, still for the purpose of procuring and studying different kinds of fish, when war broke out over Germany, and, obedient to the entreaty of his friends, he returned to Zurich. These were holiday excursions, and it rarely happened that he failed to make a yearly tour among the Alps of Switzerland in prosecution of his never-intermitted search after new species of plants.

He was too poor, however, to spend much money in travel, while he was, at the same time, bound to Zurich during a great part of the year by his professorship. It was his practice, therefore, to obtain compensation for the limited range spread before his own eyes by a full use of the eyes of other men who were at home—or who had travelled—in far countries. He established friendships with some among the learned in all parts of Europe; from such corre-spondents he received pictures of foreign animals, their local names, and other details. His house was open to all strangers, and the information published by contemporary writers—as, for example, that furnished by Bellon and Rondolet on water animals—was freely used, with full acknowledgment of every intellectual obliga-tion. No man of letters ever was more generous in recognition of the claims of others, more liberal in praise of fellow-labourers, more courteous in dissent from their opinions. In his "History of Animals" every man from whom he received help, whether in private correspondence or through public writing, has been named; and Gesner's liberality of spirit was rewarded by the full respect of the best men among the learned of his time. Bellon and Rondolet, while rivalling each other, both honoured and helped Conrad Gesner.

The "History of Animals" was planned in six books, of which four were completed. They treat—the first of viviparous and the second of oviparous quadrupeds, the third of birds, the fourth of fishes and aquatile animals. The fifth book was to have contained the history of serpents, and the sixth the history of insects. Copious materials and a large number of pictures had been collected for use under each of these heads, but they had not been arranged, nor had the writing of either volume been commenced when Gesner died. Each of the four published books is a considerable folio, containing a dense mass of print on every page. On a cursory inspection of the volumes, we observe, first, the very carefully drawn pictures, in which errors of the woodcutter, where they occur, are conscientiously pointed out, and among which it now and then occurs, as in the case of the giraffe, that a second and better sketch of some depicted animal having been procured from a trustworthy correspondent, it has been inserted in a later sheet as a correction. Every animal known to authors being included in the plan of Gesner's history, one cannot fail to be struck by the appearance, in a history of animals, of pictures of the Sphinx, of a ridiculously ugly "American monster," with a human face, of the unicorn, and of some other curiosities. They are, however, not gravely introduced as animals that have been seen, but as animals that have been described in fable or elsewhere, the precise authority for them being at all times stated, not, of course, without a degree of occasional credulity that was reasonable faith to a scholar in the sixteenth century. It is also evident, at a first glance, that in this "History of Animals" each separate animal is treated with a thoroughness of detail not common, or, indeed, likely often to be useful in our own day. Many of the single articles, reprinted in modern type, would stand by themselves as works in one volume or more. The single article upon the horse would fill, I believe, two rather thick octavo volumes. There is one quadruped, Gesner himself says, of which his account is drawn from 250 authors.

When we look more closely into the work, we find that the animals in each volume are arranged mainly in alphabetical order. Now and then, as in the case of some animals allied to the ox, in defiance of the alphabet, animals very much of the same kind have been described in association with each other; but, on the whole, the principle of arrangement is that of a dictionary. Upon this subject Gesner modestly and wisely said that he belonged rather to the grammarians than to the philosophers, of whom the number was extremely small; that, in the then existing state of knowledge, he could not undertake to make an accurate arrangement of the animal world, that he had simply endeavoured to bring together, in the same work, all that was known in his time concerning every animal, and so to produce a book of reference which would be most useful to future students if he arranged his subjects alphabetically. In volumes containing figures of animals, published separately, as companions to the "History" (in which also figures were contained), the pictures were, however, classed according to the ideas held in Gesner's time concerning genera and species.

In setting down the information he collected, Gesner divided the description of each animal into eight parts, headed by the first eight letters of the alphabet. Under letter A he wrote the name given to the animal by different nations—that is to say, its name, where it had any, in Hebrew, Arabic, and Chaldee, Persian, Greek, Latin, Italian, Spanish, French, German, English, and Flemish. When there was none already existing, he invented a vernacular name, or a suitable word for the naming of the animal in Greek or Latin. Under letter B, Gesner, in the next place, detailed in what region the animal was found, and what difference occurred in the appearance of the same animal, or what difference of species there might be corresponding to the difference between the countries it inhabited. Under the same head Gesner described the animal with very great minuteness, always proceeding from the whole to its simple parts, and then to the compound parts. Thus having described the body generally, its size, shape, colour, &c., he would proceed to a description of the skin, hair, blood, fat, bones, veins, nerves, &c., those being regarded as the simple parts; from them he would pass on to a detailed description of the eyes, ears, nose, head, horns, brain, liver, heart, &c., &c., down to feet and nails, which were made up of the simple and entitled compound parts. Included in this description of the parts of animals was an explanation of those "points" which should determine choice in the case of all animals that had been made in any way subservient to the use of man.

The next division of the information given on the subject of each animal, marked always by the letter C, detailed the natural actions of its body, its voice, senses, food, drink, sleep, dreams, excrements, and secretions, movements, as running, flying, swimming, &c., &c.

Under this division were grouped all the signs of health; and rules for the preservation of health were collected in the case of all animals that had been used by man. Under the same letter was described all that related to the subject of reproduction, from the first desire of the parents on to the final rearing of their young. All that was known of the diseases which each animal was subject to, formed then the last clause of information under letter C, the history of each disease being narrated with the treatment proper for it. Under the letter D, Gesner then described the affections, habits, and instincts of each animal, so far as they had been observed. He described, also, the behaviour of an animal towards others of its own kind, towards its young, towards man; its likes and dislikes, its tastes or distastes in relation with other animals, or with inanimate objects. Under the next letter, examination was made of the use of the animal to man, except in the two important characters of food and medicine. This division included an account of the methods of hunting some animals, or taming others, an explanation of the way in which any tame animal should be cared for and fed, with regulations for the preservation of its health. In this division were included also all matters concerning shepherds, flocks, herds, folds, stables, and so forth. With the account of horses was connected information upon the subject of carriages; with the account of oxen were connected details on the subject of the plough, and so forth; whatever contrivances or departments of industry were connected intimately with the domestic use of any animal received full notice in Gesner's History under the letter E. The same division included, of course, an account of the use of animals in spectacles and games, and did not omit to record whatever could be told about their market price. The uses of animals to man, as described by Gesner, have not, of course, been fully summed up in the preceding abstract; many animals, for example, afford prognostics of the weather. When the uses of the whole animal had been fully described, there often remained much to add about the value of its parts, and the mode of using them, as skins for clothing, dung for manure, &c. The two main uses of animals, in the opinion of

Gesner's time, their conversion into food or medicine, were discussed separately in the two next divisions of each subject. The pharmacopœia contains in our time not many medicines of animal origin, and those, like spermaceti and cod-liver oil, not very potent. Three hundred years ago, however, many parts of animals were used medicinally by the doctors. Under the letter F, therefore, Gesner considered the use of any animal as food, by whom eaten, and whether the whole was eaten, or part, and if part, what parts. He considered its use, firstly as plain food for a healthy man, and secondly, as diet for the sick. Then, to make that division of the subject quite complete, he discussed in each case the details of cookery, and the condiments with which the meat ought to be eaten. Then under letter G, the remedial uses of the animal were dwelt upon, and a collection was made of all that had been written on the use as medicine—1, of the whole animal; and 2, of any of its parts, taking first those parts which were simple, next those which were compound. In classing the different applications made of any animal or part of an animal to the diseases of man, where they had been made in more than one disease, the diseases also were named and dwelt upon in a fixed order. First, those affecting the whole system—general maladies—were considered, then maladies affecting parts, the parts being invariably taken in succession from above downwards, beginning at the head and ending at the heel. Many superstitious remedial uses have been made of animals, or of their parts; these Gesner did not omit—he wilfully omitted nothing—from his History. Having discussed fully the remedial uses of an animal itself, Gesner closed this seventh division by a history of remedies for bites or other wounds inflicted by it, giving first the general treatment of such injuries, and afterwards a detail of the single remedies that had at any time been recommended.

The last divisions of the plan upon which Gesner proposed to describe every known member of the animated world, involved often the writing for one animal of a treatise that would make an independent book. This division, under the letter H, discussed the creature philologically and grammatically. It contained the less used Latin and Greek names for it, those employed by the poets now and then, or confined to dialects; also the feigned names or nicknames given to it, and their etymologies. It discussed then grammatically the proper names of the animal in different languages, and passed on to the epithets that had been attached to them, firstly in Latin, secondly in Greek. Allied philosophically with this subject of epithets were the considerations which followed the metaphorical use of the animal's name, and of the derivative words formed from it in Greek and Latin. Information followed on the paintings, sculptures, casts, or other images made from the animal, and upon the stones, plants, or other animals deriving their own names from it, with the reason of each derivation of that kind. Gesner considered next the proper names of men, regions, towns, rivers, &c., which either had been drawn from, or accidentally resembled that of the animal whose history he was relating. In the last part of this final division the most indefatigable of scholars gave a *résumé* of the social history of each creature, of the fables with which it was connected, divinations, prodigies, portents, monsters, its connection with religious ceremonies, its burial, perhaps, in Egypt, or its sacrifice in Greece. He detailed the proverbs to which each creature had given rise, taking them chiefly from Erasmus; some being revised, and others added from the vulgar tongues or Scripture. He closed with a compilation of similitudes, emblems, and apologues.

This is the plan upon which Gesner laboured at that work which is the chief monument of his transcendent industry. Not every animal, of course, had obtained so much attention in the world as to provide matter for full treatment under every one of the eight heads, but by the plan just given the history of each was examined, and before Gesner died he had published four of the six folios which were to bring together into one place all that had been said worthy of recollection about every animal then known, whether considered as an independent creature, or in any one of its relations to society. These four volumes contain the complete history, up to the middle of the sixteenth century, of birds, beasts, and fishes.

I ought not to cease speaking of this massive work without dedicating a few words to the memory of Chrisopher Froschover, publisher of Zurich, who sustained the whole cost and risk of publication. The four folios of Gesner's "History of Animals," with the additional volumes of figures, contain a mass of typography, and a multitude of woodcuts from drawings sketched from nature, that would be regarded as the basis of a most serious enterprise by the wealthiest of publishers in the most populous metropolis of our own day. Christopher Froschover, of Zurich, did not flinch. His emblem, punning on his name of Frog-over—a boy over a frog, and frogs over a palmtree—is stamped upon the title-page of every book published by Gesner while at Zurich. When Gesner was dead, and old Christopher, his publisher, was dead, there was a young Christopher, who succeeded to the business, and mourned his father's loss through his trade emblem, by removing the old boy from the frog's back, and retaining the frog without a rider, in the foreground, while in the background there was the usual colony upon the palmtree.

It has been said that Gesner's study of Nature was confined to tangible things, animals, metals, plants. He devoted himself chiefly to the publication of a history of animals, for reasons that have been already mentioned. On metals and gems he published a small book, compiled from an immense mass of materials; and, since he did not live in the vicinity of mines, he used great zeal in the questioning of strangers, and in benefiting by the observation of his correspondents who had better opportunities of practical research. The study of plants, however, remained always his favourite pursuit. Among the mountains about Lucerne, on the banks of the Rhine, at Basle, in France, in sundry parts of Italy and about Venice, when he dwelt a month there studying fishes, in yearly trips also among the Swiss Alps, he had been always an unwearied plant collector. He had read all that was written upon botany—had at his tongue's end all the information that was to be found in Dioscorides, Theophrastus, and Pliny among the ancients, or in Ruellius, Fuchs, Tragus, and other moderns. Of every plant that he found for the first time he made a careful drawing, and caused it, if possible, to grow in his own little garden—which became a true botanic garden in the town of Zurich; or if it would not thrive there, he preserved a specimen of it carefully dried. He investigated constantly the properties of plants, studied their qualities and temperament by eating portions of them to test personally their effect upon the system, or by sitting down to his study with their stems, leaves, and flowers bound to his person, that he might observe any effect they could produce upon the skin. He sought aid from the knowledge of other men, not only in books, but in the world around him; questioning not the learned only, but conversing with the common people; learning from old crones and from rustics common names of plants, and popular traditions of their virtues; rejecting nothing scornfully, but examining all that he heard, and endeavouring to trace even the muddy waters of superstition to their wholesome source. The plants that he collected he compared with the descriptions found in ancient authors; and with each plant before him he collated the accounts of Pliny, Theophrastus, and Dioscorides, discovering blunders of compilation made by Pliny, and correcting in each author many faulty passages. His ardent interest in botany being well known among all learned men, and the courteous scholar being everywhere respected by his fellow-labourers, from Italy, France, Germany and England there were arriving constantly at Gesner's house in Zurich, seeds and plants, both dry and fresh, as new material for study. The produce of all this zeal, and of the outdoor industry of thirty years, was a collection of more than 500 plants undescribed by the ancients. He was arranging his acquired knowledge for the purpose of publishing the results of what had been, above all others, his labour of love since childhood up to the last day of his life. Many figures were already cut in wood that were to have been used on the pages of the book which Gesner did not live to write. The preparation of these figures had gone on under the close superintendence of the naturalist, whose face was often bent over his artist's shoulder, watchful to prevent the play of fancy that might introduce pictorial effect at the expense of truth. He would not leave to the discretion of the artist so much as a fibre in the venation of his leaves, or a line upon the petal of a flower, but enforced by constant scrutiny and exhortation scrupulous fidelity to Nature.

So far the story of the life of Conrad Gesner presents to our imaginations the picture of a scholar whose intense devotion to his studies might excuse in him some little neglect of what are now and then called the distractions that belong to daily life. Gesner, however, was not more a scholar than a gentleman. In the town and in the household he performed every duty with a genial promptitude. In Zurich he was honoured by all people, not as the learned man who had won European fame, and earned the title of the German Pliny, but as the kind, upright citizen. His practice as a physician was not very profitable; for it was at that time the custom among the Swiss—a custom wholesome for the time—to dread the doctor. When the doctor might, perhaps, order powder of rubies, to the despair of his poor patients, when patients suffering under the thirst of fever were forbidden to taste any liquid, and when doctors, with the best intentions, certainly killed more patients than they cured, the Swiss showed their good mother-wit by keeping physic from their doors as long as possible. The practice, therefore, of Conrad Gesner as the chief physician of Zurich, was insignificant, interfering not at all with his vocation as Professor of Philosophy, and very little with his private studies. Such cases, however, as he had, he treated with peculiar discretion; among his works there is a sanitary book "on the Preservation of Health," in which, as in his "History of Animals," he showed a due sense of the importance of a more exact study of Hygiene, and of a branch of it, I may observe, little regarded in this country—cookery.

Gesner, a Swiss and a scholar, living in the days of the Reformation, examined carefully the records of the Christian faith; he studied zealously the ancient fathers, and read the Scriptures carefully. He had a great affection for the Book of Psalms, which he read commonly in Hebrew. He was not bigoted, but lived in friendly correspondence with men of all creeds and nations, always, however, bold and earnest in support of his own views of Christian truth. He reasoned with his friends among the Unitarian heretics in Poland. While at home he did not hold himself to be too learned or too busy to attend at church, not only on the sacred days, but twice a week also on working days, when the minister, Bullinger, to whose congregation he belonged, assembled those who would attend. If he knew beforehand that Bullinger was about on any day to give an exposition of some part of the Old Testament, Gesner would take his Hebrew Bible with him to the church, and follow the preacher in it with the intellect of a philosopher and the simplicity of those past days when, as a child, he reverenced the Scriptures as he heard them from the lips of the herb-loving pastor, Fricius. The same spirit of piety had induced Gesner to take especial care that in his "History of Animals" every allusion made to an animal in holy writ should be expounded to the best of his ability.

The scholar of Zurich was a Christian and a gentleman. He shrank from giving pain, was simple in his mind and manners, free from ostentation, modest, rigidly truthful. Never idle, he had no leisure to acquire a taste for luxury, nor was there perceptible in his outward character a trace of lust. He belonged to a strict school of reformers; his speech was pure, and he abhorred either the hearing or the reading of obscenity. He reproved it when spoken in his presence; he issued Martial in a new edition, with all impure passages expunged. He lamented greatly that in his day men had reformed their opinions so much more completely than their lives; and he held frequent consultations with grave theologians on the means that might be taken to improve the discipline of the reformed church, and get better deeds as well as better doctrines from the people.

The scholar, Conrad Gesner, lived in the exercise of never-failing courtesies towards all who had relations with him. He cultivated the friendship of the good and learned, and he grudged no labour to his friends. He assisted in the revision of proof-sheets for them, suggesting from the vast stores of his knowledge any emendations or additions that seemed advantageous. He provided authorities, wrote prefaces, edited post-humous works; he helped young students by supplying them with Greek exemplars that they might earn credit by editing; he was indefatigable in his zeal to push on to success any hard-working struggler in whose merit he had faith. To the junior physicians of the town he was a guide, not a rival; he let slip no opportunity, when they met in consultation or in other ways he was able, by generous and well-timed words, to strengthen their good fame. He acknowledged every favour he received; his writings contain not one sentence of detraction, but a thousand sentences displaying cordial recognition of all merit that he found in his contemporaries.

Who that was good and learned in those days was not the friend of Conrad Gesner? The scholar's doors were always hospitably open. He desired to compensate for his own inability to travel by hearing the discourse of men from all parts of the world. He did not count the time spent in society as lost, because he did not waste his social hours in trivial conversation; he talked that he might learn. When a man came to him from a foreign country, that man was for the time his book, and while he fulfilled all his duties as a host, he was continuing his studies. Rarely a day passed in which Gesner was not visited by someone desirous either to see the famous naturalist and scholar, or to study something that he had upon his premises. As Gesner's garden had grown into a very well-supplied botanic garden, so his whole house had become a museum, although one room in it had especially been dedicated under that name to the arrangement of his dried plants, his metals and fossils, his large collection of the stuffed bodies of strange animals, and his pictures of natural objects. These treasures had accumulated rapidly by the donations of his learned visitors, and contributions sent to him from the warm friends that he had made in many corners of the world. Gesner had little gold: his treasure was his knowledge; and he gave that with unusual generosity. He was ready to explain to any people whatever they desired to understand through him, and glad to give away his duplicates to those who could appreciate such gifts. If any rare secret came to his knowledge, if a profitable hint in medicine was suddenly discovered in the course of his wide circle of reading, he never attempted to retain it and employ it to his own exclusive gain. If it was professional, it was at once communicated to his brethren in the town—if literary, it was sent to any friend who could make best and promptest use of it. Many thousands of men have had more genius than Conrad Gesner, but never one man, perhaps, has had more completely the true noble spirit of a man of letters.

In the year preceding the death of Gesner, plague increased in Zurich, and among those whom it removed was his old master, Buchman; there died also in that year Gesner's bosom friend, Johann Fricius, who had been his companion of old time in France. Gesner dreamed one night that he was bitten by a serpent, and in the morning told his wife that he regarded the dream as a presage of his death. The serpent, he said, was the plague. From that time he considered, though he was not yet forty-nine years old, and in possession of his usual health, which never had been robust, that his course of life was drawing to a close. His letters to his friends from that time frequently dwelt upon this solemn presentiment, never with pain, though he believed that his most cherished work was to be left unfinished; he expressed no regret, no dread. It is in one of Gesner's letters, written during this last year of his life— a letter to Zuinger—that a passage occurs in which we read how real had been the progress made by him in botany. Had he lived to write the work for which he had prepared himself by more than thirty years of observation, he would have achieved for himself, in the most distinct manner, a fame which we can now ascribe to him only upon the evidence of a few words in a letter. He appears to have been the first who made that great step towards a scientific botany—the distinguishing of genera by a study of the fructification. "Tell me," he writes to Zuinger, "whether your plants have fruit and flower as well as stalk and leaves, for these are of much greater consequence. By these three marks—flower, fruit, and seed—I find that saxifraga and consolida regalis are related to aconite."

On the 9th of December, in the year 1565, a plague-spot appeared on Gesner's left side, over his heart. There was no symptom of plague except the too-familiar monition of this carbuncle. The scholar, however, assured that in a few days he must quit the world in which he had been labouring so steadily, remembered that he had yet work to do, and tranquilly employed his last hours in the careful settlement of his affairs. He had not at first the usual headache, fever, or other distressing symptoms of the plague; he did not, therefore, retire to bed, but called his friends about him, and proceeded to adjust the distribution of his little property in such a way as would ensure the best attainable provision after his death for those who hitherto had been maintained by him—his wife, his only surviving sister, and his sister's children. His library he sold to his friend, Caspar Wolff, at a fair price, and then having bequeathed a fixed sum to his wife and another fixed sum to his nephews, he left to his sister the remainder of his worldly goods. He then arranged whatever papers he thought necessary to the easy settlement after his death of all money questions, writing notes and full instructions for the information and assistance of the two women who were soon to lose his protection, and despatching letters to those friends by whose advice or help their trouble would be lightened.

When he had carefully discharged this duty, Gesner closeted himself in his library with Caspar Wolff, who undertook to be his literary executor. Wolff was to inherit all the papers of his friend and teacher, and with him Gesner went through them all, arranged them, drew up a bibliographical inventory of his published works and of his unfinished writings. Above all, he assiduously laboured to make clear the design for his unwritten history of plants. The first plague-spot appeared on Gesner's breast upon the 9th of December, and he died on the 13th; but within that interval he found time not only to set his house in order, but to discuss with Caspar Wolff, and to note down for his more certain information the botanical discoveries of which Wolff had undertaken to complete the publication. When he had done all this, and written farewells to the dearest of his absent friends, though the physicians who had care of him did not despair of his recovery from an attack so mild in its approaches, Gesner talked of the new world that lay before him with the ministers of Zurich. On the day before his death, after he had been for a long time closeted with the minister, Henry Bullinger, in conversation on domestic matters which he had commended to the care of that warm household friend, he delivered, in the spirit of an early reformer, the confession of his faith.

At night, not feeling that he was upon the point of death, but watchfully solicitous for the comfort of his friends, he warned his wife away to rest, and would allow no one to sit up with him except a single nurse. Being left alone with her, he remained long awake upon his bed, praying with fervour, and then fell asleep. In the stillness of the night, he awoke suddenly, and felt that death was struggling with him. He called his wife, and desired to be carried into his museum; he had caused a bed to be made there on the preceding day; he would die among his plants and all the works of God that he had gathered there together. Supported in his wife's arms, on the bed in his museum, Gesner died that night, in the act of gentle prayer.

*Pierre Duhem*

# RENAISSANCE PHYSICS*

PROPAGATION OF THE DOCTRINES OF THE SCHOOL OF PARIS IN
GERMANY AND ITALY—PURBACH AND REGIOMONTANUS—NICHOLAS
OF CUSA—VINCI

The great Western schism involved the University of Paris in
politico-religious quarrels of extreme violence; the misfortunes
brought about by the conflict between the Armagnacs and Burgun-
dians and by the Hundred Years' War, completed what these
quarrels had begun, and the wonderful progress made by science
during the fourteenth century in the University of Paris suddenly
ceased. However, the schism contributed to the diffusion of Parisian
doctrines by driving out of Paris a large number of brilliant men
who had taught there with marked success. In 1386 Marsile of
Inghem (d. 1396), who had been one of the most gifted professors
of the University of Paris, became rector of the infant University
of Heidelberg, where he introduced the dynamic theories of Buridan
and Albert of Saxony.

About the same time, another master, reputedly of Paris, Heinrich Heimbuch of Langenstein, or of Hesse, was chiefly instrumental in founding the University of Vienna and, besides his theological knowledge, brought thither the astronomical tradition of
Jean des Linières and John of Saxony. This tradition was carefully

* Reprinted from "Physics, History of," *Catholic Encyclopedia*, XII (1911),
pp. 52-56, with the permission of The Catholic University of America Press.

preserved in Vienna, being magnificently developed there through-out the fifteenth century, and paving the way for Georg Purbach (1423-61) and his disciple Johann Müller of Königsberg, sur-named Regiomontanus (1436-76). It was to the writing of theories calculated to make the Ptolemaic system known, to the designing and constructing of exact instruments, to the multiplying of obser-vations, and the preparing of tables and almanacs (ephemerides), more accurate than those used by astronomers up to that time, that Purbach and Regiomontanus devoted their prodigious energy. By perfecting all the details of Ptolemy's theories, which they never called in question, they were most helpful in bringing to light the defects of these theories and in preparing the materials by means of which Copernicus was to build up his new astronomy.

Averroism flourished in the Italian Universities of Padua and Bologna, which were noted for their adherence to Peripatetic doc-trines. Still, from the beginning of the fifteenth century the opinions of the School of Paris began to find their way into these institutions, thanks to the teaching of Paolo Nicoletti of Venice (flourished about 1420). It was there developed by his pupil Gaetan of Tiene (d. 1465). These masters devoted special attention to propagating the dynamics of impetus in Italy.

About the time that Paola of Venice was teaching at Padua, Nicholas of Cusa came there to take his doctorate in law. Whether it was then that the latter became initiated in the physics of the School of Paris matters little, as in any event it was from Parisian physics that he adopted those doctrines that smacked least of Peripateticism. He became thoroughly conversant with the dynam-ics of impetus and, like Buridan and Albert of Saxony, attributed the motion of the celestial spheres to the impetus which God had communicated to them in creating them, and which was perpetuated because, in these spheres, there was no element of destruction. He admitted that the Earth moved incessantly, and that its motion might be the cause of the precession of the equinoxes. In a note discovered long after his death, he went so far as to attribute to the Earth a daily rotation. He imagined that the sun, the moon, and the planets were so many systems, each of which contained an earth and elements analogous to our Earth and elements, and to account for the action of gravity in each of these systems he followed closely the theory of gravity advanced by Oresme.

Leonardo da Vinci (1452-1519) was perhaps more thoroughly convinced of the merits of the Parisian physics than any other Italian master. A keen observer, and endowed with insatiable curiosity, he had studied a great number of works, amongst which we may mention the various treatises of the School of Jordanus, various books by Albert of Saxony, and in all likelihood the works of Nicholas of Cusa; then, profiting by the learning of these scholars, he formally enunciated or else simply intimated many new ideas. The statics of the School of Jordanus led him to discover the law of the composition of concurrent forces stated as follows: the two component forces have equal moments as regards the direction of the resultant, and the resultant and one of the components have equal moments as regards the direction of the other component. The statics derived from the properties which Albert of Saxony attributed to the centre of gravity caused Vinci to recognize the law of the polygon of support and to determine the centre of gravity of a tetrahedron. He also presented the law of the equilibrium of two liquids of different density in communicating tubes, and the principle of virtual displacements seems to have occasioned his acknowledgement of the hydrostatic law known as Pascal's. Vinci continued to meditate on the properties of impetus, which he called *impeto* or *forza,* and the propositions that he formulated on the subject of this power very often showed a fairly clear discernment of the law of the conservation of energy. These propositions conducted him to remarkably correct and accurate conclusions concerning the impossibility of perpetual motion. Unfortunately he misunderstood the pregnant explanation, afforded by the theory of impetus, regarding the acceleration of falling bodies, and like the Peripatetics attributed this acceleration to the impulsion of the encompassing air. However, by way of compensation, he distinctly asserted that the velocity of a body that falls freely is proportional to the time occupied in the fall, and he understood in what way this law extends to a fall on an inclined plane. When he wished to determine how the path traversed by a falling body is connected with the time occupied in the fall, he was confronted by a difficulty which, in the seventeenth century, was likewise to baffle Baliani and Gassendi.

Vinci was much engrossed in the analysis of the deformations and elastic reactions which cause a body to rebound after it has struck another, and this doctrine, formulated by Buridan, Albert of Saxony, and Marsile of Inghem he applied in such a way as to draw from it the explanation of the flight of birds. This flight is an alternation of falls during which the bird compresses the air beneath it, and of rebounds due to the elastic force of this air. Until the great painter discovered this explanation, the question of the flight of birds was always looked upon as a problem in statics, and was likened to the swimming of a fish in water. Vinci attached great importance to the views developed by Albert of Saxony in regard to the Earth's equilibrium. Like the Parisian master, he held that the centre of gravity within the terrestrial mass is constantly changing under the influence of erosion and that the Earth is continually moving so as to bring this centre of gravity to the centre of the World. These small, incessant motions eventually bring to the surface of the continents those portions of earth that once occupied the bed of the ocean and, to place this assertion of Albert of Saxony beyond the range of doubt, Vinci devoted himself to the study of fossils and to extremely cautious observations which made him the creator of Stratigraphy. In many passages in his notes Vinci asserts, like Nicholas of Cusa, that the moon and the other wandering stars are worlds analogous to ours, that they carry seas upon their surfaces, and are surrounded by air; and the development of this opinion led him to talk of the gravity binding to each of these stars the elements that belonged to it. On the subject of this gravity he professed a theory similar to Oresme's. Hence it would seem that, in almost every particular, Vinci was a faithful disciple of the great Parisian masters of the fourteenth century, of Buridan, Albert of Saxony, and Oresme.

## ITALIAN AVERROISM AND ITS TENDENCIES TO ROUTINE—ATTEMPTS AT RESTORING THE ASTRONOMY OF HOMOCENTRIC SPHERES

Whilst, through the anti-Peripatetic influence of the School of Paris, Vinci reaped a rich harvest of discoveries, innumerable Italians devoted themselves to the sterile worship of defunct ideas with a servility that was truly astonishing. The Averroists did not wish to acknowledge as true anything out of conformity with the ideas of Aristotle as interpreted by Averroës; with Pompanazzi (1462-1526), the Alexandrists, seeking their inspiration further back in the past, refused to understand Aristotle otherwise than he had been understood by Alexander of Aphrodisias; and the Humanists, solicitous only for purity of form, would not consent to use any technical language whatever and rejected all ideas that were not sufficiently vague to be attractive to orators and poets; thus Averroists, Alexandrists, and Humanists proclaimed a truce to their vehement discussions so as to combine against the "language of Paris," the "logic of Paris," and the "physics of Paris." It is difficult to conceive the absurdities to which these minds were led by their slavish surrender to routine. A great number of physicists, rejecting the Parisian theory of impetus, returned to the untenable dynamics of Aristotle, and maintained that the projectile was moved by the ambient air. In 1499 Nicolò Vernias of Chieti, an Averroist professor at Padua, taught that if a heavy body fell it was in consequence of the motion of the air surrounding it.

A servile adoration of Peripateticism prompted many so-called philosophers to reject the Ptolemaic system, the only one which, at that time, could satisfy the legitimate exigencies of astronomers, and to readopt the hypothesis of homocentric spheres. They held as null and void the innumerable observations that showed changes in the distance of each planet from the Earth. Alessandro Achillini of Bologna (1463-1512), an uncompromising Averroist and a strong opponent of the theory of impetus and of all Parisian doctrines, inaugurated, in his treatise "De orbibus" (1498), a strange reaction against Ptolemaic astronomy; Agostino Nifo (1473-1538) laboured for the same end in a work that has not come down to us; Girolamo Fracastoro (1483-1553) gave us, in 1535, his book "De homocentricis," and Gianbattista Amico (1536), and Giovanni Antonio Delfino (1559) published small works in an endeavour to restore the system of homocentric spheres.

## THE COPERNICAN REVOLUTION

Although directed by tendencies diametrically opposed to the true scientific spirit, the efforts made by Averroists to restore the astronomy of homocentric spheres were perhaps a stimulus to the progress of science, inasmuch as they accustomed physicists to the thought that the Ptolemaic system was not the only astronomical doctrine possible, or even the best that could be desired. Thus, in their own way, the Averroists paved the way for the Copernican revolution. The movements forecasting this revolution were noticeable in the middle of the fourteenth century in the writings of Nicholas of Cusa, and in the beginning of the fifteenth century in the notes of Vinci, both of these eminent scientists being well versed in Parisian physics.

Celio Calcagnini proposed, in his turn, to explain the daily motion of the stars by attributing to the Earth a rotation from West to East, complete in one sidereal day. His dissertation, "Quod cœlum stet, terra vero moveatur," although seeming to have been written about 1530, was not published until 1544, when it appeared in a posthumous edition of the author's works. Calcagnini declared that the Earth, originally in equilibrium in the centre of the universe, received a first impulse which imparted to it a rotary motion, and this motion, to which nothing was opposed, was indefinitely preserved by virtue of the principle set forth by Buridan and accepted by Albert of Saxony and Nicholas of Cusa. According to Calcagnini the daily rotation of the Earth was accompanied by an oscillation which explained the movement of the precession of the equinoxes. Another oscillation set the waters of the sea in motion and determined the ebb and flow of the tides. This last hypothesis was to be maintained by Andrea Cesalpino (1519-1603) in his "Quæstiones peripateticæ" (1569), and to inspire Galileo, who, unfortunately, was to seek in the phenomena of the tides his favourite proof of the Earth's rotation.

The "De revolutionibus orbium cœlestium libri sex" were printed in 1543, a few months after the death of Copernicus (1473-1543), but the principles of the astronomic system proposed by this man of genius had been published as early as 1539 in the "Narratio prima" of his disciple, Joachim Rhæticus (1514-76). Copernicus adhered to the ancient astronomical hypotheses which claimed that the World was spherical and limited, and that all celestial motions were decomposable into circular and uniform motions; but he held that the firmament of fixed stars was immovable, as also the sun, which was placed in the centre of this firmament. To the Earth he attributed three motions: a circular motion by which the centre of the Earth described with uniform velocity a circle situated in the plane of the ecliptic and eccentric to the sun; a daily rotation on an axis inclined towards the ecliptic, and finally, a rotation of this axis around an axis normal to the ecliptic and passing through the centre of the Earth. The time occupied by this last rotation was a little longer than that required for the circular motion of the centre of the Earth which produced the phenomenon of the precession of the equinoxes. To the five planets Copernicus ascribed motions analogous to those with which the Earth was provided, and he maintained that the moon moved in a circle around the Earth.

Of the Copernican hypotheses, the newest was that according to which the Earth moved in a circle around the sun. From the days of Aristarchus of Samos and Seleucus no one had adopted this view.

Medieval astronomers had all rejected it, because they supposed that the stars were much too close to the Earth and the sun, and that an annual circular motion of the Earth might give the stars a perceptible parallax. Still, on the other hand, we have seen that various authors had proposed to attribute to the Earth one or the other of the two motions which Copernicus added to the annual motion. To defend the hypothesis of the daily motion of the Earth against the objections formulated by Peripatetic physics, Copernicus invoked exactly the same reasons as Oresme, and in order to explain how each planet retains the various parts of its elements, he adopted the theory of gravity proposed by the eminent master. Copernicus showed himself the adherent of Parisian physics even in the following opinion, enunciated accidently: the acceleration of the fall of heavy bodies is explained by the continual increase which impetus receives from gravity.

### FORTUNES OF THE COPERNICAN SYSTEM IN THE SIXTEENTH CENTURY

Copernicus and his disciple Rhæticus very probably regarded the motions which their theory ascribed to the Earth and the planets, the sun's rest and that of the firmament of fixed stars, as the real motions or real rest of these bodies. The "De revolutionibus orbium cælestium libri sex" appeared with an anonymous preface which inspired an entirely different idea. This preface was the work of the Lutheran theologian Osiander (1498-1552), who therein expressed the opinion that the hypotheses proposed by philosophers in general, and by Copernicus in particular, were in no wise calculated to acquaint us with the reality of things: "Neque enim necesse est eas hypotheses esse veras, imo, ne verisimiles quidem, sed sufficit hoc unum si calculum observationibus congruentem exhibeant." Osiander's view of astronomical hypotheses was not new. Even in the days of Grecian antiquity a number of thinkers had maintained that the sole object of these hypotheses was to "save appearances," σώζειν τὰ φαινόμενα; and in the Middle Ages, as well as in antiquity, this method continued to be that of philosophers who wished to make use of Ptolemaic astronomy whilst at the same time upholding the Peripatetic physics absolutely incompatible with this astronomy. Osiander's doctrine was therefore readily received, first of all by astronomers who, without believing the Earth's motion to be a reality, accepted and admired the kinetic combinations conceived by Copernicus, as these combinations provided them with better means than could be offered by the Ptolemaic system for figuring out the motion of the moon and the phenomena of the precession of the equinoxes.

One of the astronomers who most distinctly assumed this attitude in regard to Ptolemy's system was Erasmus Reinhold (1511-53), who, although not admitting the Earth's motion, professed a great admiration for the system of Copernicus and used it in computing new astronomical tables, the "Prutenicæ tabulæ" (1551), which were largely instrumental in introducing to astronomers the kinetic combinations originated by Copernicus. The "Prutenicæ tabulæ" were especially employed by the commission which in 1582 effected the Gregorian reform of the calendar. Whilst not believing in the Earth's motion, the members of this commission did not hesitate to use tables founded on a theory of the precession of the equinoxes and attributing a certain motion to the earth.

However, the freedom permitting astronomers to use all hypotheses qualified to account for phenomena was soon restricted by the exigencies of Peripatetic philosophers and Protestant theologians. Osiander had written his celebrated preface to Copernicus's book with a view to warding off the attacks of theologians, but in this he did not succeed. Martin Luther, in his "Tischrede," was the first to express indignation at the impiety of those who admitted the hypothesis of solar rest. Melanchthon, although acknowledging the purely astronomical advantages of the Copernican system, strongly combatted the hypothesis of the Earth's motion (1549), not only with the aid of arguments furnished by Peripatetic physics but likewise, and chiefly, with the assistance of numerous texts taken from Holy Writ. Kaspar Peucer (1525-1602), Melanchthon's son-in-law, whilst endeavouring to have his theory of the planets harmonize with the progress which the Copernican system had made in this regard, nevertheless rejected the Copernican hypotheses as absurd (1571).

It then came to be exacted of astronomical hypotheses that not only, as Osiander had desired, the result of their calculations be conformable to facts, but also that they be not refuted "either in the name of the principles of physics or in the name of the authority of the Sacred Scriptures." This criterion was explicitly formulated in 1578 by a Lutheran, the Danish astronomer Tycho Brahe (1546-1601), and it was precisely by virtue of these two requirements that the doctrines of Galileo were to be condemned by the Inquisition in 1616 and 1633. Eager not to admit any hypothesis that would conflict with Aristotelean physics or be contrary to the letter of the Sacred Scriptures, and yet most desirous to retain all the astronomical advantages of the Copernican system, Tycho Brahe proposed a new system which virtually consisted in leaving the Earth motionless and in moving the other heavenly bodies in such a way that their displacement with regard to the Earth might remain the same as in the system of Copernicus. Moreover, although posing as the defender of Aristotelean physics. Tycho Brahe dealt it a disastrous blow. In 1572 a star, until then unknown, appeared in the constellation of Cassiopeia, and in showing accurate observations that the new astral body was really a fixed star, Tycho Brahe proved conclusively that the celestial world was not, as Aristotle would have had us believe, formed of a substance exempt from generation and destruction.

The Church had not remained indifferent to the hypothesis of the Earth's motion until the time of Tycho Brahe, as it was amongst her members that this hypothesis had found its first defenders, counting adherents even in the extremely orthodox University of Paris. At the time of defending this hypothesis, Oresme was Canon of Rouen, and immediately after he was promoted to the Bishopric of Lisieux; Nicholas of Cusa was Bishop of Brixen and cardinal, and was entrusted with important negotiations by Eugenius IV, Nicholas V, and Pius II; Calcagnini was prothonotary Apostolic; Copernicus was Canon of Thorn, and it was Cardinal Schomberg who urged him to publish his work, the dedication of which was accepted by Paul III. Besides, Oresme had made clear how to interpret the Scriptural passages claimed to be opposed to the Copernican system, and in 1584 Didacus a Stunica of Salamanca found in Holy Writ texts which could be invoked with just as much certainty in favour of the Earth's motion. However, in 1595 the Protestant senate of the University of Tübingen compelled Kepler to retract the chapter in his "Mysterium cosmographicum," in which he had endeavoured to make the Copernican system agree with Scripture.

Christopher Clavius (1537-1612), a Jesuit, and one of the influential members of the commission that reformed the Gregorian Calendar, seemed to be the first Catholic astronomer to adopt the double test imposed upon astronomical hypotheses by Tycho Brahe, and to decide (1581) that the suppositions of Copernicus were to be rejected, as opposed both to Peripatetic physics and to Scripture; on the other hand, at the end of his life and under the influence of Galileo's discoveries, Clavius appeared to have assumed a far more favourable attitude towards Copernican doctrines. The enemies of Aristotelean philosophy gladly adopted the system of Copernicus, considering its hypotheses as so many propositions physically true, this being the case with Pierre de La Ramée, called Petrus Ramus (1502-72), and especially with Giordano Bruno (about 1550-1600). The physics developed by Bruno, in which he incorporated the Copernican hypothesis, proceeded from Nicole, Oresme, and Nicholas of Cusa; but chiefly from the physics taught in the University of Paris in the fourteenth century. The infinite extent of the universe and the plurality of worlds were admitted as possible by many theologians at the end of the thirteenth century, and the theory of the slow motion which gradually causes the central portions of the Earth to work to the surface had been taught by Albert of Saxony before it attracted the attention of

Vinci. The solution of Peripatetic arguments against the Earth's motion and the theory of gravity called forth by the comparison of the planets with the Earth would appear to have been borrowed by Bruno from Oresme. The apostasy and heresies for which Bruno was condemned in 1600 had nothing to do with the physical doctrines he had espoused, which included in particular Copernican astronomy. In fact it does not seem that, in the sixteenth century, the Church manifested the slightest anxiety concerning the system of Copernicus.

THEORY OF THE TIDES

It is undoubtedly to the great voyages that shed additional lustre on the close of the fifteenth century that we must attribute the importance assumed in the sixteenth century by the problem of the tides, and the great progress made at that time towards the solution of this problem. The correlation existing between the phenomenon of high and low tide and the course of the moon was known even in ancient times. Posidonius accurately described it; the Arabian astronomers were also familiar with it, and the explanation given of it in the ninth century by Albumazar in his "Introductorium magnum ad Astronomiam" remained a classic throughout the Middle Ages. The observation of tidal phenomena very naturally led to the supposition that the moon attracted the waters of the ocean and, in the thirteenth century, William of Auvergne compared this attraction to that of the magnet for iron. However, the mere attraction of the moon did not suffice to account for the alternation of spring and neap tides, which phenomenon clearly indicated a certain intervention of the sun. In his "Questions sur les livres des Météores," which appeared during the latter half of the fourteenth century, Themon, "Son of the Jew," introduced in a vague sort of way the idea of superposing two tides, the one due to the sun and the other to the moon.

In 1528 this idea was very clearly endorsed by Federico Griso-

gone of Zara, a Dalmatian who taught medicine at Padua. Grisogone declared that, under the action of the moon exclusively, the
sea would assume an ovoid shape, its major axis being directed
towards the centre of the moon; that the action of the sun would
also give it an ovoid shape, less elongated than the first, its major
axis being directed towards the centre of the sun; and that the
variation of sea level, at all times and in all places, was obtained
by adding the elevation or depression produced by the solar tide
to the elevation or depression produced by the lunar tide. In 1557
Girolamo Cardano accepted and briefly explained Grisogone's
theory. In 1559 a posthumous work by Delfino gave a description
of the phenomena of the tides, identical with that deduced from
the mechanism conceived by Grisogone. The doctrine of the Dalmatian physician was reproduced by Paolo Gallucci in 1588, and
by Annibale Raimondo in 1589; and in 1600 Claude Duret, who
had plagiarized Delfino's treatise, published in France the description of the tides given in that work.

## STATICS IN THE SIXTEENTH CENTURY—STEVINUS

When writing on statics Cardano drew upon two sources, the writings of Archimedes and the treatises of the School of Jordanus;
besides, he probably plagiarized the notes left by Vinci, and it was
perhaps from this source that he took the theorem: a system endowed with weight is in equilibrium when the centre of gravity
of this system is the lowest possible.

Nicolo Tartaglia (about 1500-57), Cardano's antagonist, shame-
lessly purloined a supposedly forgotten treatise by one of Jordanus's
commentators. Ferrari, Cardano's faithful disciple, harshly re-
buked Tartaglia for the theft, which nevertheless had the merit of
re-establishing the vogue of certain discoveries of the thirteenth
century, especially the law of the equilibrium of a body supported
by an inclined plane. By another and no less barefaced plagiarism,
Tartaglia published under his own name a translation of Archi-

medes's "Treatise on floating bodies" made by William of Moerbeke at the end of the thirteenth century. This publication, dishonest though it was, helped to give prominence to the study of Archimedes's mechanical labours, which study exerted the greatest influence over the progress of science at the end of the sixteenth century, the blending of Archimedean mathematics with Parisian physics, generating the movement that terminated in Galileo's work. The translation and explanation of the works of Archimedes enlisted the attention of geometricians such as Francesco Maurolycus of Messina (1494-1575) and Federico Commandino of Urbino (1509-75), and these two authors, continuing the work of the great Syracusan, determined the position of the centre of gravity of various solids; in addition Commandino translated and explained Pappus's mathematical "Collection," and the fragment of "Mechanics" by Heron of Alexandria appended thereto. Admiration for these monuments of ancient science inspired a number of Italians with a profound contempt for medieval statics. The fecundity of the principle of virtual displacements, so happily employed by the School of Jordanus, was ignored; and, deprived of the laws discovered by this school and of the additions made to them by Vinci, the treatises on statics written by over-enthusiastic admirers of the Archimedean method were notably deficient. Among the authors of these treatises Guidobaldo del Monte (1545-1607) and Giovanni Battista Benedetti (1530-90) deserve special mention.

Of the mathematicians who, in statics, claimed to follow exclusively the rigorous methods of Archimedes and the Greek geometricians, the most illustrious was Simon Stevinus of Bruges (1548-1620). Through him the statics of solid bodies recovered all that had been gained by the School of Jordanus and Vinci, and lost by the contempt of such men as Guidobaldo del Monte and Benedetti. The law of the equilibrium of the lever, one of the fundamental propositions of which Stevinus made use, was established by him with the aid of an ingenious demonstration which Galileo was also to employ, and which is found in a small anonymous work of the thirteenth century. In order to confirm another essential principle of his theory, the law of the equilibrium of a body on an inclined plane, Stevinus resorted to the impossibility of perpetual motion, which had been affirmed with great precision by Vinci and Cardano. Stevinus's chief glory lay in his discoveries in hydrostatics; and the determining of the extent and point of application of the pressure on the slanting inner side of a vessel by the liquid contained therein was in itself sufficient to entitle this geometrician from Bruges to a foremost place among the creators of the theory of the equilibrium of fluids. Benedetti was on the point of enunciating the principle known as Pascal's Law, and an insignificant addition permitted Mersenne to infer this principle and the idea of the hydraulic press from what the Italian geometrician had written. Benedetti had justified his propositions by using as an axiom the law of the equilibrium of liquids in communicating vessels, and prior to this time Vinci had followed the same logical proceeding.

## DYNAMICS IN THE SIXTEENTH CENTURY

The geometricians who, in spite of the stereotyped methods of Averroism and the banter of Humanism, continued to cultivate the Parisian dynamics of impetus, were rewarded by splendid discoveries. Dissipating the doubt in which Albert of Saxony had remained enveloped, Vinci had declared the velocity acquired by a falling body to be proportional to the time occupied by the fall, but he did not know how to determine the law connecting the time consumed in falling with the space passed over by the falling body. Nevertheless to find this law it would have sufficed to invoke the following proposition: in a uniformly varied motion, the space traversed by the moving body is equal to that which it would traverse in a uniform motion whose duration would be that of the preceding motion, and whose velocity would be the same as that which affected the preceding motion at the mean instant of its duration. This proposition was known to Oresme, who had demonstrated it exactly as it was to be demonstrated later by Galileo; it was enun-

ciated and discussed at the close of the fourteenth century by all
the logicians who, in the University of Oxford, composed the school
of William of Heytesbury, Chancellor of Oxford in 1375; it was
subsequently examined or invoked in the fifteenth century by all
the Italians who became the commentators of these logicians; and
finally, the masters of the University of Paris, contemporaries of
Vinci, taught and demonstrated it as Oresme had done.

This law which Vinci was not able to determine was published
in 1545 by a Spanish Dominican, Domingo Soto (1494-1560),
an *alumnus* of the University of Paris, and professor of theology
at Alcalá de Henares, and afterwards at Salamanca. He formulated
these two laws thus:

The velocity of a falling body increases proportionally to the
time of the fall.

The space traversed in a uniformly varied motion is the same
as in a uniform motion occupying the same time, its velocity being
the mean velocity of the former.

In addition Soto declared that the motion of a body thrown ver-
tically upward is uniformly retarded. It should be mentioned that
all these propositions were formulated by the celebrated Dominican as if in relation to truths generally admitted by the masters
among whom he lived.

The Parisian theory, maintaining that the accelerated fall of
bodies was due to the effect of a continual increase of impetus
caused by gravity, was admitted by Julius Cæsar Scaliger (1484-
1558), Benedetti, and Gabriel Vasquez (1551-1604), the celebrated Jesuit theologian. The first of these authors presented this
theory in such a way that uniform acceleration of motion seemed
naturally to follow from it.

Soto, Tartaglia, and Cardano made strenuous efforts, after the
manner of Vinci, to explain the motion of projectiles by appealing
to the conflict between impetus and gravity, but their attempts were
frustrated by a Peripatetic error which several Parisian masters had
long before rejected. They believed that the motion of the projectile
was accelerated from the start, and attributed this initial accelera-

tion to an impulse communicated by the vibrating air. Indeed, throughout the sixteenth century, the Italian Averroists continued to attribute to the ambient air the very transportation of the projectile. Tartaglia empirically discovered that a piece of artillery attained its greatest range when pointed at an angle of forty-five degrees to the horizon. Bruno insisted upon Oresme's explanation of the fact that a body appears to fall in a vertical line in spite of the Earth's motion; to obtain the trajectory of this body it is necessary to combine the action of its weight with the impetus which the Earth has imparted to it. It was as follows that Benedetti set forth the law followed by such an impetus. A body whirled in a circle and suddenly left to itself will move in a straight line tangent to the circle at the very point where the body happened to be at the moment of its release. For this achievement Benedetti deserves to be ranked among the most valuable contributors to the discovery of the law of inertia. In 1553 Benedetti advanced the following argument: in air, or any fluid whatever, ten equal stones fall with the same velocity as one of their number; and if all were combined they would still fall with the same velocity; therefore, in a fluid two stones, one of which is ten times heavier than the other, fall with the same velocity. Benedetti lauded the extreme novelty of this argument with which, in reality, many scholastics had been familiar, but which they had all claimed was not conclusive, because the resistance which the air offered to the heavier stone could certainly not be ten times that which it opposed to the lighter one. Achillini was one of those who clearly maintained this principle. That it might lead to a correct conclusion, Benedetti's argument had to be restricted to the motion of bodies in a vacuum, and this is what was done by Galileo.

*Grant McColley*

# HUMANISM AND
# THE HISTORY OF ASTRONOMY*

During the span of three centuries, science has changed from a generally neglected discipline to one of the strongest forces which shape the modern world. In fields ranging from medicine to industry, it is in fact reshaping large sections of the world, and if used wisely will ultimately advance the living conditions of all mankind. Too much cannot be said of its present and potential importance, even more in peace than in the inferno of war.

Yet science, and I speak here particularly of applied science and technology, is inadequate to discipline man. Among other things, history is essential. Lacking the discipline of history, the human mind seldom reaches its highest development; it may even remain somewhat naïve. Fortunately for mankind, the contributions which science can make toward a more mature civilization are not limited to the discovery and application of new laws, formulae, methods and techniques. These contributions include the history which science has created as it has developed.

Social and economic theories, as well as those political, theo-

* Reprinted from *Studies and Essays in the History of Science and Learning Offered in Homage to George Sarton,* edited by M. F. Ashley Montagu (New York, 1946), pp. 323-57.

logical and philosophical, often prove abstract and subjective. Inevitably, they permit, and invite, many different interpretations and shades of interpretation. Combined with other variables, these factors frequently have made it either difficult or impossible for the detached historian to determine which theory or concept was relatively correct and which relatively incorrect. He found it difficult to isolate and evaluate the varied forces which moved or controlled the mind of man. Comparatively, the major theories which make up focal points in the history of science are definite and objective. The historian of science can say with some confidence which theory was relatively or wholly correct, which rival conception largely incorrect. He has the better, the more precise yardstick for measuring the achievements of man, and thus is better equipped to inform man concerning himself.

The classic *Warfare of Science with Theology in Christendom* of Andrew D. White illustrates aptly the intellectual discipline which the history of science may bring to the discerning mind. In her *Gradual Acceptance of the Copernican Theory of the Universe,* Dean Dorothy Stimson shows what understanding may come from tracing the background and development of an astronomical theory. The present essay follows the general path to which Miss Stimson brought so much illumination.

There is great intrinsic value in the history of the several astronomical hypotheses which preceded, competed with, and ultimately gave way to the Copernican theory. In addition, this story holds much enlightenment and humanistic discipline. Fragmentary and incomplete as it is, the present sketch of these once active hypotheses may in some measure indicate that the history of science is both knowledge and intellectual discipline.

I

Among the ancient "scientific" authorities with which the orthodox of the sixteenth century challenged Copernican astronomy,

Aristotle and Ptolemy were ostensibly the most important. The word ostensibly is purposely used, for both Aristotle and Ptolemy appear not infrequently as cloaks designed to perpetuate certain vested interests, cultural and theological as well as scientific. Behind and closely interwoven with the thought of these interests was a complex of old ideas and beliefs which time and custom had made a part of the attitudes and conceptions of the great majority. In the best sense of the word, the opposition which gathered behind Aristotle and Ptolemy was not scientific.

To the Middle Ages and the Renaissance, Aristotle properly was known as "the philosopher." A restless and vigorous thinker, his inquiries encompassed all known fields of human speculation, and necessarily led him into the field of astronomy. Ptolemy was the geographer and astronomer, little more, but this was sufficient to make him second only to Aristotle in an almost superstitious veneration.

Within Christian Europe, the veneration for Aristotle and Ptolemy seems however to have resulted more from respect for the current thought system which these men were used to support, and less from a careful analysis of their astronomical and related writings. The man who read these works critically would have found that while the "physics" of Aristotle and Ptolemy were relatively compatible, their astronomical systems proved different and irreconcilable. Equally, if not more important was the fact that Ptolemy himself set forth or was credited with conflicting cosmologies. To a much lesser degree, this is true of Aristotle. As a result, there was not only the question of Aristotle versus Ptolemy, but the questions of Ptolemy versus Ptolemy, and Aristotle versus Aristotle. What the orthodox of the Middle Ages and Renaissance largely did was to make (or follow) selections from these religiously cited authorities. As the centuries passed, these selections were modified and supplemented, and woven into a system which included ideas and values unrelated to the thinking of either Aristotle or Ptolemy. Such manipulations of course did not cease with the Middle Ages and the Renaissance.

In the field of astronomy, Aristotle was primarily the historian and recorder rather than the inventor of systems. Of the two second-hand and partially different cosmologies which he supported, that best known is described in *De Caelo*. The system which he presents in *De Caelo*—one traditionally regarded as indebted to Egyptian thought—followed the ancient school which placed the sun immediately above the moon, and the moon immediately above the earth.

Under this system, spheres were assigned to the seven "wandering stars" or planets: the moon, sun, Venus, Mercury, Mars, Jupiter and Saturn. Beyond the final planetary sphere was placed the sphere of the fixed stars. In subsequent Aristotelian-Ptolemaic as tronomy, this sphere was never described in detail, probably because observation gave so little information concerning it. However, the sphere apparently was called fixed because the relative position of one star to another appeared unchanged.

By way of partial digression, it may be noted that some modern historians have assumed that followers of the mediaeval Aristotelian-Ptolemaic cosmologies believed all the fixed stars equidistant from the central earth. They have failed, however, to quote any first-hand source which specifically makes this statement. The present writer has found none (at least as yet). On the contrary, much first-hand evidence describes the sphere of the fixed stars as a zone of relatively great depth in which the stars were placed at irregular distances from the earth. More often than not, the depth of the sphere equalled the distance from the earth to its internal boundary or concavity.

In *De Caelo,* Aristotle described the universe as spherical and within it placed a central earth, eight major planetary spheres, the sphere of the fixed stars, and circumscribing all, the primum mobile or prime mover. The last has been interpreted as either a spiritual force or a physical phenomenon, but the exponents of Aristotelian-Ptolemaic cosmologies seem to have regarded it as physical. As the primum mobile turned the planetary spheres and that of the fixed stars from east to west, completing one revolution about the earth in twenty-four hours, a so-called natural motion carried each "planet" a short distance from west to east. (Aristotle regarded movement from east to west as the more "honorable.") The moon, for example, made each day one complete westward movement about the earth, and at the same time travelled eastward approximately twelve of the three hundred and sixty degrees of the celestial circle.

In his *Metaphysics,* Aristotle developed a system of physical concentric (or homocentric) spheres which, as he frankly stated, was drawn from Callippus and Eudoxus. For the "seven planets," Eudoxus appears to have postulated a total of twenty-six homocentric spheres. Callippus expanded this number to thirty-three; Aristotle, to fifty-four, or a total of fifty-five including the sphere or zone of the fixed stars.

The major purpose of the twenty-two spheres added by Aristotle apparently was to provide an explanation for the "natural" or west to east motion of the planets postulated by both Aristotelian and Ptolemaic cosmologies. The question of the force which produced the east-west as well as the west-east movements, Aristotle answered by assuming the existence of spirits or "intelligences" which turned the spheres of the system. Although this elaborate system of impervious homocentrics found occasional advocates, particularly after the breakdown of other Renaissance rivals of the Copernican theory, it developed no effective influence. Among other things, too many astronomers may have felt much as Thomas Campanella did. Discussing the cosmological system described in the *Metaphysics,* the fiery Dominican declared in his *Apologia pro Galileo:*

Aristotle multiplies intelligences, which in truth are only appearances. Nor does he provide reasons for these appearances, as Saint Thomas, Simplicius, and other commentators confess. He makes war between God [? the Prime Mover] and the angels, by causing them to move contrary to his motion. They are said to imitate God, but in fact they oppose him. Likewise, there is war between the angels. One angel rushes to the east, another to the west, one to the

north, a fourth to the south, and labor to move the spheres in contrary directions. Some are set to turning, and an equal number to
resisting. In this way Aristotle brings violence into heaven, and
discord . . . among the angels.

In contrast with the astronomical theories which Aristotle supported and expanded, the physical doctrines which he advocated
long exerted a sustained and powerful influence. Developing the
ancient and conventional idea that the physical world is made up
of the four elements of earth, water, air, and fire, Aristotle assigned
to these elements specific zones within the sublunary world. Earth
and water, he asserted, inherently sought the center, and had a
natural movement downward. Similarly, air and fire sought to leave
the center of the world, and naturally moved upward. The sublunary
world, or that part of the universe below and circumscribed by the
sphere of the moon, was thus divided into the regions of earth,
water, air, and fire. To the four physical elements, Aristotle added
an apparently non-physical fifth, the quintessence.

Earth, water, air and fire became "simple" elements. The stars
likewise were classified as composed of one element or as "simple
bodies." Logic then persuaded Aristotle that a body composed of
only one thing could naturally have only one simple motion. As
Aristotle thought, there were two kinds of simple motion, recti-
linear (up or down) and circular. The senses proved that water and
earth moved up and down; therefore the earth could not have the
circular motion required for axial rotation. The stars, by contrast,
had the simple circular motion.

The substance or stuff of the stars and all other heavenly bodies,
said Aristotle, consisted of the fifth essence or quintessence. Non-
physical in nature, the quintessence was considered eternal and
immutable. Applying further his conception that the sphere is the
most perfect three-dimensional figure and the circle the most perfect two-dimensional, Aristotle declared that the heavenly bodies
must be perfect spheres, and must move in perfect circles.

Inadequate and inaccurate as was his cosmological thinking, justice to Aristotle requires recognition of the fact that his system or systems constituted an improvement over much preceding thought. Nevertheless, his astronomical and physical systems were only superficially quantitative. They are best described as a mixture of speculative metaphysics and logic. From this came both their strength and their weakness. Added appeal came from the fact that Aristotle had welded the whole into a system, or pattern of thought.

In partial contrast with Aristotle and his school stood the Ptolemists. This school made at the first a definite and conscientious attempt to construct an astronomical system based upon the direct observation and analysis of celestial phenomena. In place of transparent, solid homocentric spheres, the predecessors of Ptolemy developed a theory of imaginary eccentric circles and epicycles. Apollonius of Perga appears to have originated this theory. Later came Hipparchus, by common consent the greatest celestial observer of antiquity, and in the second century of the Christian era, Claudius Ptolemy. In his *Syntaxis Mathematica,* better known as the *Almagest,* Ptolemy combined the observations of Hipparchus and the imaginary eccentrics and epicycles of Apollonius into the first workable astronomical system. Some years later, however, either Ptolemy or some one thought to be Ptolemy set forth a somewhat different theory in the second part of a work entitled *Hypotheses of the Planets*. During the latter Middle Ages and the Renaissance, both theories were indiscriminately called "the Ptolemaic." The resulting confusion has today not been wholly dissipated.

As mentioned in most histories of science, the major basis for the system of the *Almagest* was the Apollonian eccentrics and epicycles, plus the observations of Hipparchus. Hipparchus began with the movement of the sun in its apparent annual revolution about the earth, measuring its daily motion throughout the year. He confirmed the belief of previous astronomers that the motion of the sun was irregular, and noted the place where it apparently progressed with the greatest velocity. He also observed that this point did not remain fixed, but that it advanced slowly along the orbit of its annual revolution about the earth. Similarly painstaking observations proved that the moon, as well as the sun, did not appear to move about the center of the earth with circular and uniform motion. Observation of the planets, including their seeming variation in size and brightness, led to the same conclusion regarding the orbits of the "wandering stars."

It seems that a system of simple eccentric circles was first tried, but this proved inadequate to explain and represent geometrically the movements of the heavenly bodies. An epicycle, or smaller circle, then was added. The epicycle had for its center of revolution a point on the circumference of the major eccentric circle. The planet was represented, geometrically rather than actually, as moving around on the circumference of the epicycle. The major circle, known as the deferent, carried both the minor circle, or epicycle, and its planet around the central earth.

This combination of larger and smaller circles provided one explanation for elliptical planetary orbits, but its great importance was the apparent explanation of the peculiar movements of the planets when the earth was regarded as the approximate center. With the earth taken as the point of reference, a planet appeared to change markedly its speed of movement. More than this, it seemed now to move forward, on occasion to pause, and later to move backward. In the words of the Ptolemaic astronomer, the planet was progressive, stationary, and retrograde.

The true explanation of these apparent celestial acrobatics is of course the orbital motion of the earth and the observed second planet about the sun. As Venus and the earth move on the same side of the sun, the smaller orbit of Venus draws it ahead of the earth in its revolution about the common center. Venus is then "progressive," to use the Ptolemaic term. As the planet passed to the side of the sun opposite that facing the earth, her relative motion appeared "retrograde," or backward. Between the change from the apparent progressive to retrograde movements, or from retrograde to progressive, Venus appeared, in relation to sun and earth, to be stationary. In *Paradise Lost,* completed almost a century and a quarter after the *De Revolutionibus* of Copernicus, Milton refers to this conception when he describes the state of the universe immediately following its creation by Christ:

> *The heavens and all their constellations rung,*
> *The planets in their stations listening stood.*

In the system which Ptolemy developed in the *Almagest,* spheres had no place. So far as the text indicates, the eccentrics and epicycles postulated in the work were regarded as nothing more than geometrical representation useful in charting the movements of the planets. The so-called fixed stars, or stars of the eighth sphere, Ptolemy apparently regarded as moving freely in space. However, as Copernicus was to do fourteen centuries later, Ptolemy largely confined himself to developing a planetary system and said little about the fixed stars. It is noteworthy that although the earth was taken as the center of the stars and of the universe, it did not have for its center, the center of the planetary orbits. Here Ptolemy again varied from Aristotle. Had he regarded the center of the earth as the center of these orbits, he would have used concentric rather than eccentric circles.

As set forth in the *Almagest,* the combined work of Ptolemy and his predecessors marked a definite advance in astronomy. For its day, and for many subsequent centuries, it provided a basis for calculations far more accurate than was possible with other systems. Since eccentrics and epicycles were regarded as useful geometrical representations rather than exact physical descriptions, the way was left clear for untrammeled investigation of celestial movements. The *Almagest* also served to impress upon those who studied it some conception, however faint, of the vast magnitude of the world. The earth was considered infinitely small in relation to the universe. Conversely, the universe was regarded as infinitely large in relation to the earth.

One passage in Book I of the *Almagest,* as translated by Dean Stimson, emphasizes the greatness of the universe as one basis for the argument that the heavy earth can stand unmoved and unsupported in the center of the world:

Those who consider it a paradox that a mass like the earth is supported on nothing, yet not moved at all, appear to me to argue according to the preconceptions they get from what they see happening to small bodies about them, and not according to what is characteristic of the universe as a whole. This is the cause of their mistake. I think that such a thing would not have seemed wonderful to them any longer if they had perceived that the earth, great as it is, is merely a point in comparison to the surrounding body of the heavens.

They would find that it is possible for the earth, being infinitely small relative to the universe, to be held in check and fixed by the forces exercised over it equally and following similar directions by the universe, which is infinitely great and composed of similar parts.

Because of its relative excellence, and the deserved authority which followed from this, the *Almagest* served to perpetuate the circular astronomy which it utilized. It also supported the ancient school of physical thought which postulated the four elements of earth, water, air and fire, and defined their properties. Here Ptolemy agreed with Aristotle. The "light" naturally moved up, and the "heavy" moved down, although strictly speaking there was to Ptolemy "neither up nor down in the universe." As Aristotle had done before him, Ptolemy set forth with confidence and at length plausible arguments against the axial rotation of the central earth.

For approximately three centuries, Ptolemy has been best and generally known in astronomy for the *Almagest*. It is natural that during this period, and particularly during its latter part, many men have regarded the *Almagest* as the immediate or ultimate source of most Ptolemaic astronomy which preceded and for almost a century triumphed over Copernicus and *De Revolutionibus*. Nevertheless, the *Almagest* was not the source of this dominant type of Ptolemaic astronomy. This important source was the *Hypotheses of the Planets*. The author of the *Hypotheses* describes it as a summary of the *Almagest,* but this statement is true of only Book I. Book II of the work presents an astronomical system quite different in vital conceptions from that set forth in the *Almagest*. The *Hypotheses* may not have been written by Ptolemy. Such a competent historian of astronomy as J. L. E. Dreyer believes that it was. Allowing for corruption and alteration in the texts which survived, the writer considers Dreyer's conclusion sound. The important point, however, is that the theory set forth in Book II of the *Hypotheses* became the better known and more influential "Ptolemaic system."

In the *Hypotheses,* Ptolemy or whatever astronomer wrote the book turned from the idea of using merely geometrical representations of celestial phenomena. He attempted to set forth an actual representation of the constitution of the universe, "as real," Dreyer observed, "as that described in Aristotle's *Metaphysics.*"

The basic conception set forth may have been original with Ptolemy, but it certainly was not new. In fact, it resembles that described somewhat earlier by Theon of Smyrna. Under this idea, the epicycle which carried a planet upon its revolving circumference did not center in the circumference of the eccentric (or deferent); on the contrary, it was placed securely between eccentrics—now spheres instead of circles. The epicycle and the two eccentrics were described as hard but transparent physical shells, possibly regarded as similar in composition to the impervious homocentrics postulated by Aristotle.

As the major eccentric or deferent revolved, this sphere literally rolled the now spherical epicycle between its surface and that of its companion eccentric. Outside, or above, the external eccentric of the planet, the *Hypotheses* then placed a third major sphere. This sphere touched the external eccentric on only one side—enough for physically communicating revolution to it. The center of the third sphere was the earth; in short, this sphere was a homocentric. A similar homocentric, or concentric, was placed within the internal eccentric. With the several planets thus equipped, all the machinery proposed for the planetary system fitted neatly and tightly together. Mechanically and geometrically, the theory seemed perfect.

As historians of astronomy repeatedly have pointed out, Ptolemy and in part Aristotle came first to Europe through the medium of the Arabs. The ideas of Aristotle, particularly as urged and modified by Averroes and others, were given prominence. The conceptions which unquestionably represented Ptolemy—those of the *Almagest,* were on the whole ignored by the Arabian custodians of Grecian thought. Perhaps they found too indefinite the idea that planetary spheres of circles were purely geometric representations. Whatever the cause, the Moslems generally adopted and spread the physical system presented in Book II of the *Hypotheses.*

In supporting and presenting this second Ptolemaic system, different Arabian writers naturally made greater or lesser alterations in the theory. For the most part, they tended to retain in some form the basic conception of a solid spherical epicycle—that to which the planet was attached—rotating or rolling between the hard surfaces of two eccentric spheres. From the point of view of posterity, the two most important Arabian advocates probably were Al Fargani and Al Battani, for through these men elements of the second Ptolemaic system passed into the *Sphere* of John of Holywood, commonly known as Sacrobosco.

Within two centuries after invention of the printing press, Europe was covered with literally hundreds of editions of commentaries on Sacrobosco's *Sphere.* Virtually all of these texts, which increased with the years, used without qualification the machinery of planetary motion set up by the second Ptolemaic system. As late as 1581, such an erudite mathematician and astronomer as Christopher Clavius entitled his scholarly book on astronomy a *Commentary on the Sphere of John of Sacrobosco,* and utilized the planetary machinery of the second Ptolemaic system. In this text, the original twenty-four pages of Sacrobosco were expanded to new lengths—approximately six hundred pages in all. From 1581 until the last independent edition of 1611, the frequently reprinted *Commentary* of Clavius stood as the most influential textbook on astronomy known to Europe.

In keeping with all commentators on Sacrobosco noted by the present writer, Clavius quotes and amplifies the Aristotelian conception that above the "elementary" region (that below the moon) the universe and all within it are composed of a non-physical and immutable fifth essence. The basic text for his comment, taken from Sacrobosco, states:

> Circa elementarem vero regionem aetherea regio lucida, ab omni variatione, sua immutabili essentia immunis existens, motu continuo circulariter incedit; Et haec a philosophis quinta nuncupatur essentia.

With the customary and seeming inconsistency of those who mixed Aristotle with the planetary machinery of Book II of the *Hypotheses,* Clavius placed spheres described as solid about the planets and within the heavens previously said to be composed of the non-physical and immutable fifth essence. He says of the representative epicycle: "Epicyclus autem est sphaerula solida inter crassitiem eccentrici simpliciter immersa, ita ut circa suum proprium centrum circumvolvi possit. . . . In epicyclo affixus est Planeta & ad eius motum circa centrum G, defertur, ideoque a Ptolemaeo appellatus est. . . ."

This apparent inconsistency, however, is trivial in comparison with others. Chief among these was the widespread union of Christian theology with the Aristotelian-Ptolemaic cosmologies—a union which was preserved by leaders among the Lutheran and other protestant sects. As the indefatigable if obscurantist Cosmas labored to prove near the beginning of the Middle Ages, the cosmology which can be gleaned from Scripture is quite different from any Aristotelian-Ptolemaic universe. For one thing, Aristotle and Ptolemy (correctly) described the earth as round. Scripture speaks of its corners, so that no literal Biblical cosmology can describe the earth as a sphere.

With complete disregard for such passages as Cosmas had used, Roman Catholic astronomers and theologians of the thirteenth and succeeding centuries put the Christian world squarely behind the Aristotelian-Ptolemaic conception of the universe. The slight tie consisted primarily of the several Scriptural passages, most of them obviously figurative, which either described the earth as immobile or the sun and stars as in motion. The Bible of course names no system of planets. Thomas Aquinas, for example, was careful to keep

Aristotle distinct from Scripture, but as decades and centuries passed, the immutable heavens and perfect spheres of Aristotle, the ancient physical notions supported by both Aristotle and Ptolemy, and the complicated mechanism of the Ptolemaic spheres became to the devout almost as sacred as the fragmentary cosmological passages found in Holy Writ.

To the non-Christian universe built from Aristotle and Ptolemy, plus ideas from other writers, Christian astronomers added the Caelum Empyreum or Heaven of Heavens. This Heaven of Heavens was placed immediately beyond and encircling the primum mobile, the virtually two-dimensional sphere which lay immediately beyond the bounding convexity of the sphere or zone of the fixed stars. Regarded as infinite in depth, the Heaven of Heavens also was described by astronomers as the home of God, of the angels, and generally of the elect. Christopher Clavius said in part that in the Caelum Empyreum there "is infinite space . . . in which God exists in his essence." In the diagram of the universe of the earlier (1539) *Petri Apiani Cosmographia, per Gemman Phrysium . . . restituta,* reproduced by Francis R. Johnson in his *Astronomical Thought in Renaissance England,* the Caelum Empyreum is described as "habitaculum Dei et *omnium electorum."* Moving upward, or outward, from the central earth, one passed from the earth through the corruptible sublunary "world"; reaching the moon, he entered the pure and incorruptible heavens; crossing and leaving these, he at last came to the infinite deep and pure Caelum Empyreum, or Heaven of Heavens. A beautiful and poetic gradation.

This complex Aristotelian-Ptolemaic-Biblical universe fabricated by the Middle Ages might not unappropriately be termed the first wonder of the collective human imagination. Man's uncorrected senses, together with Scripture, informed him that the earth was immobile, and the moon, sun, and stars revolved about it. More precise and detailed observation, as made from the earth, indicated planetary orbits which appeared highly irregular. Systematized and put to practical use, these observations provided a relatively accurate calendar and workable catalogues of the movements of planets and stars. The system did pass the pragmatic test of usefulness, or workability. Again according to the senses, water stood above earth and air above both. Fire or flame rushed upward through the air. Scripture spoke of a Heaven and a realm of God. From such slight foundations grew one of the most powerful and impressive structures of thought that man has created.

Regarding the nature of mankind, perhaps the most striking implication of the history of the Aristotelian-Ptolemaic-Biblical universe is that man possesses an inordinate love for a system. It also appears that if man makes a sufficiently long and determined attempt, he can produce a system which will explain to his satisfaction a given set of phenomena. The prestige and long life of this cosmology also may reflect on the part of many men a feeling of need for being associated and in harmony with an authoritative system. This feeling may at times be connected with a desire to have and to retain the privileges brought by vested interest.

Within this eclectic universe were many conceptions either contrary to or incompatible with ideas held by Aristotle and Ptolemy or set forth in Scripture. In short, the system itself denied the authority of Aristotle and Ptolemy, as Aristotle and Ptolemy, not to mention that of all Holy Writ. Yet most advocates of the system appeared to believe firmly in the infallibility of its three major pillars. They failed to see, or in some instances probably preferred not to see that the universe was not an Aristotelian-Ptolemaic-Biblical system, but a system which man had selected primarily from these sources.

During the two-thousand-year span which began with Aristotle and closed with the complete disintegration of the Aristotelian-Ptolemaic-Biblical universe, the predominate tendency of those who proposed alteration was to seek changes in detail. Sometimes these changes consisted of substitutions; sometimes they were additions or amplifications. Yet even when the system had become as obviously unsatisfactory as it was cumbersome, only a very limited few proposed a change in basic theory.

Equally important is the indicated predilection for the unification of such different fields as astronomy, or physics, and theology, and the resulting attempt to judge what is relatively true in one by what is believed correct in another. The history of Aristotelian-Ptolemaic-Biblical astronomy, particularly when this astronomy was sharply challenged during the Renaissance, definitely illustrates the apparently natural tendency of men to judge truth in one field by what they consider truth in a second. For centuries Christian theology believed itself best served by a cosmology which placed the earth, immobile, in the center of the universe. What appeared theologically true and desirable, must therefore be astronomically true, or so many sincere and able men reasoned.

If these varied implications have general validity, they will appear in the history of the systems which during the late Renaissance developed the power first to challenge and later to overthrow the long-dominant universe gathered chiefly from Aristotle, Ptolemy and the Scriptures.

## II

During the sixteenth and early seventeenth centuries, when the combination Aristotelian-Ptolemaic-Biblical cosmology had become more and more obviously unworkable, an increasing number of relatively independent thinkers began turning to other theories. For the most part, these theories had been enunciated and partially outlined by the ancients, although none seems to have been developed into a system. They included not only the heliocentric theory, but also the theory of the diurnal rotation of the central earth, the geo-heliocentric hypothesis, and apparently the theory which Otto von Guericke was (about 1660) to call the Fourth System of the World—a combination of the geo-heliocentric hypothesis and the theory of the diurnal rotation of the central earth. In terms of the contemporary thought pattern, the heliocentric or Copernican theory was the most heterodox; the geo-heliocentric the least.

Among the less heterodox theories, the oldest is apparently the theory of the diurnal rotation of the central earth. This theory, which was not confused by its Renaissance advocates with the Copernican hypothesis, was also the first to achieve any widespread acceptance in the modern world. Where used in an otherwise neo-Ptolemaic system (*Almagest* rather than Book II of the *Hypotheses*), the theory substituted rotation of the central earth for the violent diurnal revolution of the planets and stars, plus that of the hypothetical primum mobile.

The concept of the diurnal rotation of the central earth appears to have had one or more advocates among Greeks of the sixth century B.C. On the authority of Eudemus, both Theon of Smyrna and Anatolius named Anaximander (610-? 546 B.C.) as its earliest advocate. Under the caption, "Who found What in Mathematics," Theon wrote that "Eudemus says in his books on astronomy . . . that Anaximander was the first to state [? find] that the earth hangs in space, and turns [? moves] about the center [? axis] of the universe." Quoting Theophrastus, Cicero described Hicetas of Syracuse as supporting the theory; Diogenes Laertius describes it as advanced by Leucippus, and stated that Philolaus "was the first to assert that the earth moves in a circle, although other authorities say it was Hicetas of Syracuse."

The pseudo-Plutarch of the *Placita,* followed by Eusebius and Hippolytus, made Ecphantus of Syracuse a third member of this group of fifth century advocates of the theory. The first writer, whose account is quite similar to that of the second, states that Ecphantus "gave a motion to the earth, not progressive, but in the manner of a wheel moving upon its own axis. Thus the earth turns itself from west to east upon its own center." Among later advocates of the conception a number of early historians, particularly the doxographic writers, included Heraclides of Pontus, Aristarchus of Samos, and Seleucus. There is no question that these three Greeks believed in the axial rotation of the earth. However, Seleucus seemingly was the only member of this group who restricted his conception to the theory of the diurnal rotation of the central earth.

It is difficult to say precisely what prestige this conception enjoyed during antiquity. However, it is the only theory which both Aristotle and Ptolemy regarded as sufficiently important to attack at length, with the attack of the first made in *De Caelo* and that of the second in the *Almagest*. The authority acquired by these men doubtless worked against sympathetic consideration of the theory, and yet, the mediaeval and Renaissance popularity of *De Caelo* and the Renaissance knowledge of the *Almagest* did much to keep the theory before the eyes of men interested in astronomy.

Although the absence of adequate evidence makes any conclusion impossible, it seems that the theory of the diurnal rotation of the central earth remained relatively quiescent from the days of the Romans until perhaps the thirteenth century. Here again, however, we can judge only by the attacks made upon the conception. Several Arabian writers, including Al Katibi and Abu-l-Faraj, briefly described and condemned it. In Christian Europe, Thomas Aquinas supported Aristotle in his rejection of the theory. However, as Campanella later emphasized, Thomas was careful in his commentary on *De Caelo* to place Aristotle, and not Scripture, against the theory. Equally important for the thirteenth century, although increasingly less so for subsequent periods, was the attack made by Giovanni Campano da Novara, Chaplain to Urban IV. In his *Tractatus de Sphaera,* written after 1261 and apparently first published at Venice in 1518, Campano opens his criticism with the statement:

> There are some people who have a vexatious disposition of mind; they are more apt to imagine the impossible than to comprehend the necessary. They declare that the sphere of heaven does not move, but that the earth, on the contrary, moves herself with all that she contains, and each day makes one complete revolution.

This section of the *Tractatus,* together with those which follow it, suggests irritation at possibly contemporary proponents of the theory. The following sections largely repeat the old arguments about the ship, the moving arrow or flying bird, and the movement of stones. These arguments held that the aerial movements of the arrow, of birds and of stones would be drastically affected by axial rotation.

During the fourteenth century, discussion of the theory of the diurnal rotation of the central earth seems to have increased. Among other writers, its claims were discussed by Albert of Saxony in his commentary on Aristotle's *De Caelo*. As Professor Lynn Thorndike has noted, the theory was attacked vigorously by the anonymous author of *Six Books on Metaphysics and Natural Philosophy*. To the unnamed writer, this "most false" conception neither explained such phenomena as eclipses, conjunctions and oppositions, nor why the sun and moon are nearer at some times than at others. All this is of course true, if the theory included nothing except the earth's axial rotation. With many predecessors, the author declared (incorrectly in this case) that the great velocity of a spinning earth would bring buildings down in ruins.

In contrast with this and other attacks stood the favorable presentation of the theory by one or more scholars at the University of Paris, if we may trust the reports made by Francis Mayron and Albert of Saxony. After the year 1350, the conception unquestionably was supported by Nicolas Oresme. The arguments presented by Bishop Oresme include one which was to become standard with many subsequent advocates of the theory. This was the axiom that God and Nature do nothing the more difficult way. One who has witnessed the final stages of gestation may be inclined to question this axiom, but such variants did not trouble its advocates. Wrote the Bishop:

[Under the old hypothesis,] it is reasonable to suppose that the heavens, which are greater and placed farther from the center, [must] make their revolutions in greater time than those nearer the center, for if they make them in a period equal or less, [as the old hypothesis requires,] their [speed of] movement will be very excessive. . . . To put in place of this revolution, one small operation —the daily movement of the earth, which is very small compared with the sky, and to avoid multiplication of operations diverse and outrageously immense—is to follow what God and Nature made and ordained.

In passing, we may infer that Copernicus possibly read with profit either the first part of this argument, or a statement similar to it. He of course develops the argument into a *reductio ad absurdum*.

During the fifteenth century, the theory of the diurnal rotation of the central earth was rejected by John Mueller, better known to the Renaissance as Regiomontanus, and generally regarded as the leading astronomer of Europe. It was to him, before Copernicus, that the Pope had taken his request for a more accurate calendar. The heavy censure of Regiomontanus was given in Book I of his *Epitome* of Ptolemy's *Almagest,* written before 1476 and apparently first published in 1496. However, it may be that this opposition failed to represent the personal beliefs of the author, for in the *Opusculum Geographicum* of 1553, Schoener declared that Regiomontanus had accepted the earth's axial rotation. It was then somewhat hazardous to endorse publicly any heterodox hypothesis. But whatever the private beliefs of Regiomontanus, Europe generally regarded this influential astronomer as opposed to the theory.

In the fifteenth, as during the preceding century, learned and powerful churchmen differed over the theory. But once more the great majority opposed it. Its able opponents included the Spanish Bishop Tostatus (Tostado), and Peter, Cardinal de Aliaco. Differing with these men, Nicolas, Cardinal of Cusa, found place in *De Docta Ignorantia* to support the major element of the theory, and to set the earth in axial rotation within a universe which possessed no physical center. For the customary physical center of the universe, Cardinal Cusanus substituted a spiritual one.

The sixteenth century brought the first modern reference which the writer has found which neither supports nor challenges the theory. This description occurs in the encyclopedic *De Expetendis et Fugiendis Rebus Opus* of George Valla. Under the caption, "De motu terrae," the author attributed to Philolaus the Pythagorean the belief that the earth is borne about the fire in an oblique circle, in the same manner as the sun and moon. He then stated that Heraclides of Pontus and Ecphantus the Pythagorean also believed in the earth's motion, but gave to it a wheel-like rotation about its axis from west to east.

Near the close of the first quarter of the sixteenth century, Caelio Calcagnini, professor at the University of Ferrara, gave vigorous support to the theory. His brief treatise, published with a collection of other papers, has the title, *Quod caelum stet, terra moveatur commentatio ad Bonaventuram Pistophilum.* This apparently public letter opened with the declaration that the heavens, which are thought to turn so swiftly about the earth, stand still and remain perpetually quiet. The earth, which men believe firm and immobile, rotates on its axis. In partial support of his belief that the earth could move, Calcagnini cited the well-known mechanical dove of Archytas.

The most important argument, at least from the author's point of view, Calcagnini built from Plato. He first argued that if the world is an animal, as the *Timaeus* states, it is certain that in the middle, as in other animals, is placed a heart which everywhere moves (or quickens) the adjoining members. By adding subsequent links to his chain of thought, Calcagnini reached the proposition that the central heart of the world moves, and that the central earth turns in perpetual motion.

In his commentary-epistle, Calcagnini also introduced the familiar "Argument from Authority." He first mentioned Nicetas, and erroneously, Archimedes, stating that these men believed the earth the one thing in the universe which moved. Apparently following the account written by Cicero, the author repeated the tradition—one also supported by Aristotle and others—that in the *Timaeus,* Plato supported the conception. Later, Calcagnini gave what, to the present writer, is the first example of an author citing a "modern" in support of the theory. This honor fittingly went to the intellectually fearless Nicolas, Cardinal of Cusa, whom Calcagnini described as the "perspicuous and ingenious man Cusa."

To some degree because the greater number of presses had brought a marked increase in published textbooks and commentaries on astronomy, the sixteenth century multiplied attacks upon the theory of the diurnal rotation of the central earth. Nevertheless, there is some evidence that this increase resulted more from the growing prestige of the conception. During the fifteenth and sixteenth centuries, the most popular basis for astronomical commentaries and treatises was the slender *Sphere* of Joannes de Sacrobosco (John of Holywood). Among many other things, this work differed from Ptolemy's *Almagest* in that it said nothing regarding the theory of the earth's axial rotation. The book merely asserted that "the earth stands (*teneatur*) in the middle of all things (*in medio omnium*)." Any reference to the earth's axial rotation in a commentary on Sacrobosco therefore represented a conscious addition by the editor.

Among the more than one hundred editions of commentaries on Sacrobosco which the present writer has had the opportunity to examine, the earliest to make this suggestive addition was that written by Franciscus Capuano of Manfredonia. In the Venice edition of 1493, the author apparently fails to mention the theory. He confines discussion to Sacrobosco's brief statement. However, and contrary to M. Duhem, the subsequent edition of 1499 discusses the theory. In fact, approximately two folio pages are devoted to attacks upon the conception. Some of Capuano's arguments might have come from Ptolemy's *Almagest,* as yet not well known in Christian Europe, but all could have derived from Aristotle's *De Caelo,* which is mentioned specifically. In the Venice edition of 1531, that used by Duhem, Capuano continued his attack upon the theory of the earth's axial rotation. A more popular commentary on Sacrobosco, one which appears the most popular of the late fifteenth and early sixteenth centuries, has a similar history. This is the commentary of Jacques Lefèvre. When Lefèvre wrote the first edition of the *Sphere,* apparently about 1493, he ignored the theory. In later editions he specifically mentioned and rejected the conception. Citing rather than quoting or paraphrasing Aristotle, Lefèvre declared that the earth could not turn upon its own center and that it stood stable in the middle of the world.

Among the various arguments advanced by these two commentators, the most novel is one employed by Capuano. Using a setting perhaps suggested by one of the arguments for a rotating earth (the relativity of motion as shown by a moving ship), Capuano gave a new application to the old argument that if the earth rotated, a stone tossed perpendicularly into the air would move westward during both ascent and descent. If a man high on a ship should drop a stone when the vessel was moving rapidly, declared Capuano, then the stone would fall astern of the ship at a point far removed from where it was dropped. The unsoundness of this illustration shows that it never was tested and that it was developed purely for purposes of refutation.

However, the most important development of the sixteenth century was the introduction of passages from Scripture as arguments against the theory. Although it is not uncommon to describe the Middle Ages as intellectually backward and that indefinite period known as the Renaissance as comparatively progressive and enlightened, such men as Thomas Aquinas did not cite Scripture against the theory of the earth's diurnal rotation. It is of course possible that until the sixteenth century, most opponents of the theory did not feel it sufficiently important to require Scriptural refutation.

Apparently beginning among the Lutherans a few decades after 1500, the religious opposition to the theory spread throughout Europe and encompassed writers of all major nations and sects. Toward the end of the century, it appeared in the exhaustive commentary on Sacrobosco prepared by the most able of late sixteenth-century Roman Catholic astronomers, Christopher Clavius. Said Clavius:

We read in Psalm 103 [104.5]: "Who laid the foundations of the earth, that it should not be moved for ever." Likewise [we learn] in Ecclesiastes I: "The earth abideth forever. The sun also ariseth, and the sun goeth down, and hasteth to the place where he arose; and there whirling about continually, goeth toward the south, and turneth about unto the north." What could be stated more clearly? Also most clear is the testimony that the sun is moved which Psalm 18 gives us, where we read: "The sun is as a bridegroom coming out of his chamber, and rejoiceth as a strong man to run a race. His going forth is from the end of the heavens, and his circuit unto the ends of it; and there is nothing hid from the heat thereof."

Perhaps better evidence of the growing strength of the theory of the diurnal rotation of the earth is the appearance of attacks upon it in poetry and other forms of literature. The Scottish poet George Buchanan castigated those who held the earth does not stand fast. Near the close of the sixteenth century, the most famous of contemporary French poets, Guillaume de Saluste, seigneur du Bartas, twice condemned the theory in his widely read *La Semaine* (1578). In the popular English translation of Joshua Sylvester, Du Bartas declared in one section of the *First Week:*

> *So far do they from sense and reason err,*
> *Who think the heavens stand, and that the earth doth stirr. . . .*
> *But who has seen a selfly-turning stone?*
> *How then should earth turn her whole lump alone?*
> *Let's therefore with old truth affirm,*
> *That th' earth remains unmoveable and firm.*

As he opened the second and more extended reference, Du Bartas apparently sought to discredit the relativity of motion argument drawn from a ship sailing out from the shore:

> *Those clerks that think (think how absurd a jest)*
> *That neither heaven nor stars do turn at all,*
> *Nor dance about this great, round, earthly ball;*
> *But the earth itself, this massy globe of ours,*
> *Turns round about once every twice-twelve hours:*
> *And [they think] we resemble land-bred novices*
> *New brought aboard to venture on the seas;*
> *Who at first launching from the shore suppose,*
> *The ship stands still, and the earth it goes. . . .*

Among others, Du Bartas may have been stimulated to write this passage by Rabelais, who had stated in Book V of *Pantagruel:*

"Truly," said Pantagruel, "you tell no news. In our world, we see five hundred such changes and more every year." Then, considering the different manner of these moving ways, he told us he believed Philolaus and Aristarchus had philosophized on this island, and indeed that Selucus was of opinion that the earth rotates about its poles, and not the heavens—whatever we may think to the contrary. When we are on the river Loire, we think the trees and shore move, although this is only the effect of the boat's motion.

Quite naturally, the theory now was gaining the sympathy and support of writers more scientific in their interests than was Rabelais. In his *New Philosophy,* published in Rome in 1591 and at Venice two years later, Franciscus Patricius defended the axial rotation of the earth. Apparently indebted to Copernicus for his major argument, Patricius stated that if the stars moved, they either must be attached to a huge revolving sphere, or be moved freely through space. However, a sphere of the size required to contain them could not withstand the enormous speed of a diurnal revolution about the earth. Similarly, if the stars were not placed within a sphere, the most distant among them could not move at the enormous velocity demanded by daily revolution. In keeping with a conception at least as old in the Christian world as St. Augustine, and common to the Ptolemaic astronomer, Patricius assumed without discussion that the so-called fixed stars are located at different distances from the central earth.

Three years after publication of the *New Philosophy* of Patricius, there was printed in England the *Astrolabium Uranicum Generale* of John Blagrave. This English astronomer has been described as a supporter of Copernicus, who is favorably mentioned in the *Astrolabe,* and indeed he may have been. In his book, however, Blagrave went no further than his countryman William Gilbert was soon to go in *De Magnete,* and confined his discussion to the axial rotation of the earth. What Blagrave actually does is not to advocate the heliocentric theory of Copernicus but rather to use one of the arguments advanced by Copernicus (and others) to support the hypothesis of the earth's axial rotation. Blagrave is of course endorsing the argument of Copernicus:

> . . . confirming Copernicus's argument, who sayeth that the weakness of our senses do imagine the heavens to move about every twenty-four hours from east to west by a primum mobile, whereas indeed they have been always fixed, and it is the earth that whirleth about. . . .

During the year 1600 there appeared in London the first English book on science to attain high international prestige. This book was of course the Latin *De Magnete* of William Gilbert. Here, the English physician and scientist attempted to provide some concrete explanation for the axial rotation of the earth. According to his well-known conclusion, the earth is a great magnet. Since the magnetized spheres, or terrellas, with which he experimented had rotated under the influence of a magnetic field, Gilbert decided that magnetism explained the earth's axial rotation. In addition, magnetic attraction could so bind objects to the earth that they would be unaffected by its movement. A stone thrown perpendicularly into the air would therefore fall back upon a rotating earth at precisely the spot from which it had been thrown. The flight of birds or arrows and the movement of clouds would likewise be unaffected by the earth's axial rotation. By demonstrating the existence of forces of attraction, even though the forces proposed have proved unsatisfactory, Gilbert seriously weakened the orthodox position.

Apparently the oldest of the heterodox astronomical theories, the hypothesis of the diurnal rotation of the central earth was the first to become an effective rival of Ptolemaic and related cosmologies. This rank was relatively short-lived, but was held for approximately a half-century. In comparison with the early importance of the Copernican theory, the greater strength of the axial rotation conception is not inadequately reflected by the *Sphere* of Francesco Giuntini. Published in the late sixteenth century, this commentary devoted two half-pages to the Copernican hypothesis and more than four to the theory of the diurnal rotation of the central earth.

A second important competitor of Ptolemaic cosmology was the relatively innocuous geo-heliocentric hypothesis. Perhaps known to the Egyptians as well as the Greeks, it was also a conception with a long history. Among the Greeks, it apparently attracted less attention than the theory of the diurnal rotation of the central earth. A similar situation seems to have existed in Europe during the era of the thirteenth to sixteenth centuries. During the intervening Roman and early Christian era, however, the geo-heliocentric hypothesis seems to have been the more popular among the heterodox conceptions. This situation reappeared during the second half of the seventeenth century. By this time, a number of supporters and potential supporters of the axial rotation theory had moved closer to or had adopted the Copernican system. With the Ptolemaic type of astronomy completely discredited, and the Roman Catholic Church officially or at least semi-officially opposed to any movement of the earth, all faithful Roman Catholic astronomers of necessity turned to the geo-heliocentric hypothesis. This is not to say that astronomy, as well as the attitude of their church, was not an important factor in determining their position.

According to the geo-heliocentric hypothesis, the two inferior planets of Venus and Mercury moved in orbital revolution about the sun, and as they did so, turned with the sun about the central, immobile earth. This is the distinguishing feature of the hypothesis. Since the superior planets then known—Mars, Jupiter and Saturn, were considered in all reputable systems (including the Ptolemaic) as moving about both sun and earth; the geo-heliocentric hypothesis made centers of both sun and earth. Hence, its name. The most complete early description of the distinguishing feature of this hypothesis was made by Vitruvius during the first century of the Christian era:

The stars of Mercury and Venus make their retrograde motions and retardations about the rays of the sun, forming by their courses a wreath or crown about the sun itself as the center. It is because of this revolution about the sun that they pause at their stations in the space occupied by the signs.

During the next century, the Platonist Theon of Smyrna gave a much less precise description of the hypothesis (or its distinguishing feature).

Neither Vitruvius nor Theon attributed advocacy of the geo-heliocentric theory to any early Greek. During the fourth and fifth centuries, however, Chalcidius and Martianus Capella ascribed it—apparently erroneously—to Heraclides of Pontus. As Heath and others have shown, Heraclides went further than the geo-helio-centric hypothesis, for he supported both the revolution of Mercury and Venus about the sun and the rotation of the earth on its axis. This is the theory which Otto von Guericke eventually termed the "Fourth System of the World."

The geo-heliocentric hypothesis came to the Middle Ages supported by the prestige of Vitruvius, Macrobius, and Capella. As Pierre Duhem demonstrated after painstaking investigation, the hypothesis and closely related conceptions continued active. In addition to a number of mediaeval manuscripts which described Mercury and Venus as sometimes below and sometimes above the sun, there were works which stated clearly and unmistakably that these two planets revolve about the sun. The earliest yet noted of such works, one apparently written by an unnamed astronomer to the last Latin emperor of Constantinople, Baldwin of Courtenay, included this statement: "The circles of Venus and Mercury . . . move about the sun, and have for the center of their orbits the center of the sun." As Duhem observed, the account indicates clearly that this anonymous astronomer believed Mercury and Venus revolved on epicycles about the sun, and moved with the sun about the earth.

In that portion of his intensive investigation which have been published (and all should be), Duhem does not carry his invaluable history of the geo-heliocentric theory beyond the fifteenth century. It would seem certain there are a number of unnoted fifteenth- and sixteenth-century advocates of this well-known hypothesis. The present writer has had the good fortune to find one of these, the mathematician George Valla. In addition to the encyclopedic *De Expetendis et Fugiendis Rebus Opus,* mentioned earlier, Valla edited the first Latin edition of Aristarchus's *On the Sizes and Distances of the Sun and Moon.* In the *Opus,* published at Venice in 1501, Valla not only described the distinguishing feature of geo-heliocentric astronomy, but presented it as a conception which he personally accepted. Discussing the topic, "Of the Motions of the Planets," Valla stated that Mercury and Venus "are moved about the sun," and that "in one fashion, Venus and Mercury encircle the sun; in another way, they are encircled by the sun." What Valla said in effect is that Mercury and Venus revolve about the sun, and as the sun carries them in their epicycles about the earth, it in turn encircles the two planets.

Despite its able and important advocates, the geo-heliocentric hypothesis apparently was not developed into a cosmological "system" until the closing years of the sixteenth century. To repeat a commonplace to historians of science, the man who produced this system was Tycho Brahe, the greatest celestial observer of the Renaissance. The Danish astronomer first advanced the conception in a work completed about the year 1588, *De Mundi aetherei recentioribus Phaenomenis.* By way of preface, Tycho noted that the Ptolemaic system was too involved an explanation of celestial motions. The heliocentric system of Copernicus, he continued, opposed the principles of physics, and, definitely conflicted with statements in Scripture. In addition, the apparent absence of annual stellar parallax made it necessary to assume an inestimably vast space between Saturn and the fixed stars—in short, to expand the universe to almost infinite or in-de-finite depth.

Pondering such problems about the year 1583, Tycho said there had then come to him, "as if by inspiration," a different idea concerning planetary motions. We cannot know what part, if any, Tycho's possible unconscious recollection of the undeveloped geo-heliocentric hypothesis played in this inspiration. He could scarcely have been totally ignorant of it. Whatever the true answer may be, it is certain that Tycho was the first to develop the hypothesis into an astronomical system. In this system, the earth stood at the center of the sphere, or zone, of the fixed stars, and also at the center of the orbits of the moon and sun. The sphere of the fixed stars and the "planets" moved about the earth in diurnal revolution. The sun was the center of the orbits of the five known planets; that is, of both the three known superior as well as the two inferior planets. The inferior planets, Mercury and Venus, moved about the earth by virtue of their epicycle movement about the sun. This system, Tycho held, satisfactorily accounted for the progressive, stationary, and retrograde phenomena which Ptolemaic astronomers explained by the use of epicycles, and Copernicus by assigning an annual orbital motion to the earth.

As Dreyer pointed out a half-century ago, Tycho did not publish *De Mundi aetherei recentioribus Phaenomenis,* but instead sent copies to various friends and correspondents. One result of this plan was that Tycho's geo-heliocentric system was not widely known until the publication in 1602 of the *Progymnasmata.* Within a decade, when Galileo and the telescope completed the downfall of the tottering Ptolemaic hypothesis, the orbital movement of Venus and Mercury about the sun became the required minimum for a creditable astronomical system. Reputable astronomers were forced to go as far as Tycho. As events fell out, this minimum was virtually the maximum for astronomers dominated by literal interpretation of Scripture, or guided by the attitude of powerful elements within the Roman Catholic Church. In short, the geo-heliocentric theory became among the rigidly orthodox or theologically confined astronomers the heir of the Aristotelian-Ptolemaic system.

Last in Renaissance influence among the three intermediate theories was the hypothesis which Otto von Guericke not inaptly termed the "Fourth System of the World." This hypothesis combined into one system the two theories just discussed: the theory of the diurnal rotation of the central earth and the geo-heliocentric system. In addition to most of the advantages which Tycho Brahe claimed for the latter, this system naturally eliminated the violent daily revolution of planets and stars assumed by Aristotelian-Ptolemaic and other fixed-earth systems.

The Fourth System of the World seems to have had very few advocates prior to the late Renaissance. However, as Heath has indicated, this hypothesis did have the support of the important Greek philosopher, Heraclides of Pontus. The various references to Heraclides and his theories suggest some scattering support for them. However, in this as in other similar cases, the doxographic fragments which describe the cosmological beliefs of Heraclides give no indication of whether or not he developed the hypothesis into a system. The inference is that he did not.

As the task of formulating an astronomical system from the geo-heliocentric hypothesis apparently was left undone until Tycho Brahe, so that of building the "Fourth System" seemingly was left to Tycho's contemporary and partial rival, Nicolas Reymers. In the year 1586, Reymers set up the Fourth System in model form for the Landgrave at Cassel. Two years later, he explained it in detail in his *Fundamentum Astronomicum* and, in 1597, again advanced it in his *De Astronomicis Hypothesibus*. Reymers, whom Dreyer has justly described as an able mathematician, set forth with his system many ideas concerning the physical nature of the world much more advanced than those of Tycho. At this place, however, it is sufficient to note that until an earlier diagram is found antedating that which Reymers included following folio 40 of the *Fundamentum,* we may say that he was the first astronomer to publish a diagram which both pictures constellations of stars dispersed in space at varying distances from the earth and includes neither concavity nor convexity of the eighth sphere. Some Ptolemists had of course shown stars scattered within the depth of the eighth sphere at varying distances from the earth.

The attraction of the Fourth System to able minds prior to the telescope is at least suggested by the inability of William Gilbert to choose between this hypothesis and the Copernican theory. The reference naturally is not to sections of *De Magnete,* but to the extended discussion in the posthumously published *De Mundo Nostro sublunari Philosophia Nova.* Superficially, Gilbert's choice in his *Philosophia Nova* appears to waver between the Copernican and the Tychonic type of geo-heliocentric system. However, since he stoutly advocated the axial rotation of the earth, his actual choice lay between the heliocentric theory on one hand and the Fourth System on the other. A few years after the death of Gilbert, David Origanus supported the two major concepts of the Fourth System in his *Ephemerides* (1609).

Of the three rival theories which stood between the Copernican hypothesis on one hand, and Aristotelian-Ptolemaic cosmologies on the other, two were distinctly different. As previously stated, the third was a combination of these two. However, all three had one thing in common among themselves, and indeed, in common with the Aristotelian-Ptolemaic. They did not disturb the most important addition which Christian theology had made to the pagan cosmos. This vital addition consisted of the Caelum Empyreum, or Heaven of Heavens, which Christian astronomers and theologians had for centuries placed above and circumscribing the physical universe. As previously stated, this Heaven of Heavens lay almost immediately beyond the zone which contained the fixed stars, was considered as infinite in depth, and was described as the home of God and his angels, and in some cases of the elect.

In the three intermediate theories, only the conception of the earth in axial rotation conflicted with passages of Scripture, literally interpreted. This conflict, as Nicolas Reymers and others pointed out, could easily be resolved. A number of the passages which described the earth as fixed could be understood as referring to fixed in a given place rather than as fixed as to motion. Others could be interpreted as descriptive of time. Because of their setting, most of those describing the sun as in motion might be taken as poetical or figurative, and no more literal than the references to corners and pillars of the earth ignored by the Christian Ptolemists.

In varying degrees, all three of these theories dispensed with the poetic conception of the nature of the heavens postulated by Aristotle and his followers. The appearance and disappearance of new stars had called seriously into question the idea that stars are immutable; the observed movement of comets (thought to belong to the sublunary world) in the "heavens" cast doubts upon the artificial separation of the universe. The telescope completed what many painstaking observers had well developed with purely ocular observations. At the most, poetic Aristotelian concepts were little more than interesting decorations; they involved no theological beliefs regarded as vital. They apparently had been retained in part because of the general authority of Aristotle, in part because of their poetic nature, and in part because of two forces which operate against any change: inertia, and the tendency of most human minds to resist different ideas and to retain those received in early years.

In summary, it may be said that all three of the intermediate systems conflicted with the body of cosmological decorations known as Aristotelian. Two of the conceptions, the theory of the diurnal rotation of the central earth and the Fourth System of the World conflicted in part or in whole with literal interpretations of various Scriptural passages. One, the geo-heliocentric hypothesis, did not.

Approximately a half-century ago, J. L. E. Dreyer raised the question why, in the *Dialogo* of 1632, Galileo pitted the Copernican against the Ptolemaic, when for some years it had been obvious that the geo-heliocentric (Tychonic) was becoming, and on the Continent had become, the major rival of the heliocentric. At this distance, one cannot pretend to know the different motives which affected Galileo. It is, however, a fact that where the "optic tube" had demonstrated only one feature of the Copernican theory, it had proved the truth of the distinguishing characteristic of the geo-heliocentric—the revolution of Mercury and Venus about the sun. All that Galileo could honestly say was that the geo-heliocentric theory failed to go far enough.

A second fact is that the leading astronomers of the Roman

Catholic Church had gradually moved to support and advocate the geo-heliocentric hypothesis. Galileo needed the permission of the Church for publication of his *Dialogo*. In view of the difficulties which he had in obtaining ecclesiastical permission for the printing of his book, it appears almost certain that Galileo would never have received this had he attacked what was surely becoming the semi-official system of his church. The system whose disintegration the telescope had completed was the Aristotelian-Ptolemaic. This system also had been and was being rejected by the most orthodox of Roman Catholic astronomers. Twenty years before publication of the *Dialogo,* Christopher Clavius had raised himself from the bed on which he was to die, or so the story goes, and declared that a substitute system for the Ptolemaic must be found. What is more important, and certainly is true, is that Clavius said almost as much in the final edition of his works which followed the telescope.

III

The history of the heliocentric hypothesis has been told both in digest and *in extenso* so many times that anything more than the most compressed sketch is almost as much out of place as it is unnecessary. The author of the theory, as such, appears to have been Aristarchus of Samos; the author and developer of the heliocentric system was Nicolas Copernicus. In this system, the sun was placed in the center of the planets, all of which moved in orbital revolutions of varying periods. The order was the central sun, Mercury, Venus, the earth and its moon, Mars, Jupiter, and Saturn. As Copernicus definitely stated, his hypothesis concerned the planets, and did not include the fixed stars. However, these were regarded as relatively immobile. The earth had a diurnal rotation on its axis, and by Copernicus was given a third movement of wobbling, somewhat as a top just before it concludes spinning.

However, Copernicus did extend to an in-de-finite if not, in

Renaissance terms, an almost infinite distance, the space between the sphere of Saturn and the nearest fixed stars. Stated differently, the Copernican system assumed that the fixed stars were an in-de-finite or almost infinite distance from the planetary system. The apparent absence of annual stellar parallax made any other assumption impossible. This assumption pushed the fixed stars into the space which Christian astronomy and theology had assigned to the Caelum Empyreum or Heaven of Heavens. It mixed the "mundane" and spiritual worlds. The minds of most sixteenth-century astronomers appeared to pause before this seeming requirement of the Copernican system.

The power of the idea that the Heaven of Heavens was located, or began, within the space where Copernicus at least by implication placed the stars, is aptly illustrated by the astronomer, Thomas Digges. This courageous Englishman, whose importance in the Elizabethan scientific movement has been so effectively established by Professors Johnson and Larkey, therefore diagrammed the in-de-finite or perhaps infinite "eighth sphere" of the Copernican system as a mixture of fixed stars and the Heavens of Heavens. In his diagram, Digges states that "This orbe of starres fixed infinitely up extendeth hit self in altitude sphericallye, and therefore immoveable[,] the pallace of foelicitye garnished with perpetuall shininge glorious lightes innumerable farr excellinge our sonne both in quantitye and qualitye[,] the very court of coelestiall angelles devoyd of greefe and replenished with perfite endlesse ioye[,] the habitacle for the elect." As Johnson and Larkey correctly state in their noteworthy edition of Digges's *A Perfit Description,* the English astronomer does go beyond Copernicus in that he unequivocally describes the Copernican eighth sphere as infinite. Although other factors may well have entered, it is true that any part of the universe which included the infinite Heaven of Heavens, or, more precisely, which merged with this Heaven, must in Christian thought of the Renaissance be described as infinite.

The Copernican theory also invited another problem. This

problem, like that brought by the Copernican extension of the mundane universe, was one avoided by the three systems intermediate between the heliocentric and Aristotelian-Ptolemaic. By making the sun the center of the earth's system, and placing the planets then known in revolution about it, Copernicus put the earth and the "planets" on the same plane. If the earth is a planet, said some, then the planets are earths. To an age which loved analogy (and what age does not), this situation frequently connected the Copernican theory with one or more phases of the doctrine of a plurality of worlds, without as well as within our solar system. To a number of writers, the doctrine of a plurality of worlds in turn suggested the worlds which Leucippus, Democritus and Epicurus described as not created by a Christian God but by the fortuitous concurrence of atoms. Other essential foundations of Christian theology, to say nothing of Christian ethics, seemed also to be involved.

On one hand, Christian theology of the Middle Ages and Renaissance described man as the heir to original sin. As such, man was condemned at birth. On the other hand, man was said to be the special creation of God, and a being so loved by his divine Father that God gave His only Son in atonement for man's sin. Another mark of God's love and favor was the creation of the earth and universe especially for man, and the creation and subjection of the animals to him. This balance seemed necessary for a just religion.

To the difficult theological problems posed by the doctrine of a plurality of worlds, a variety of answers was possible, including:

(1) Deity created only one inhabited world, our earth.

(2) Deity created a plurality of inhabited worlds, but man sinned only in this world.

(3) Deity created a plurality of inhabited worlds; mankind sinned in them all.

(4) Through His death on our earth, the Son atoned for all men in all worlds, if man sinned in all worlds.

Even prior to the seventeenth century, there were deeply religious men who sincerely believed that the doctrine of a plurality of worlds could be harmonized with the system of Christian theology held by most believers. During the fifteenth century, William Vorilong attempted this task. His solution ignored the question of the special creation of man on this earth, and held that men could be created on other earths who did not sin, and were untainted by the sin of Adam. He made the reservation, however, that if men in other worlds had sinned, Christ could have died on this earth for the inhabitants of an infinity of worlds. In discussing the last question, Vorilong wrote: "It would not be fitting for Him to go into another world that He must die again."

Unfortunately, a complete solution was more complicated. To assume that Deity had permitted sin to enter only this one world might imply reflection on the universality of Divine Justice. To assume that there existed in all worlds either a sequential or simultaneous repetition of an Adam and Eve, an apple (fruit), and a Devil disguised as or in a serpent was a problem of less theological difficulty than that of Divine Justice. Nevertheless, it would have proved troublesome to current theological systems.

Faced by difficult theological as well as scientific problems, it is understandable that the late sixteenth- and early seventeenth-century astronomers who had rejected Aristotelian-Ptolemaic astronomy generally turned to one of the theories less radical than the Copernican. Of the two types of problems, it seems that to men of the period, the theological were given more weight than the scientific.

It is against theological opposition to the Copernican theory that Campanella chiefly addressed himself in the *Apologia pro Galileo*. As much can be said for many other writers, both preceding and following Campanella. Among the latter was young John Wilkins, later the major organizing force behind the Royal Society, brother-in-law of Oliver Cromwell and Bishop of Chester. Well aware that even in protestant England the theological issues were at least as important as the scientific, Wilkins attacked them boldly, and to those who followed him, successfully. Among others, Boyle continued this effort to harmonize Christian theology with Copernican astronomy, both in his own writing and through establishment of the Boyle Lectures.

With the support and effective aid of the Royal Society, Isaac Newton published in 1687 his famous *Principia,* whose full title translates as *Mathematical Principles of Natural Philosophy*. In this work, the Copernican theory was demonstrated mathematically, verifiable natural laws were set forth, some of which, incidentally, were in part the fruit of the labor and genius of Kepler and other predecessors. In one meaning of the word, philosophy was joined to astronomy, somewhat as it had been in the Aristotelian-Ptolemaic cosmology of the Middle Ages and Renaissance. Of course, science had replaced pseudo-science, except for speculations regarding other solar systems.

By the *Principia,* astronomy, physics, and even philosophy were joined. Only theology was lacking to complete the four elements which made up the cosmological pattern of thought during the Middle Ages and Renaissance through Aristotelian-Ptolemaic astronomy. Following the example of Bishop Wilkins and others, Newton addressed himself to this task in the second edition of the *Principia,* and in harmony with his courageous predecessors, he closed the gap by bringing theology to the findings which laborious and honest research had found written in the second "Book of God."

Particularly did Newton seek a solution for the problem brought by the vastly extended Copernican universe, one whose immensity seemingly left no place for the concept of the Heaven of Heavens. "This most beautiful system of the sun, planets, and comets," wrote Newton in the opening paragraphs of his General Scholium, "could only proceed from the counsel and dominion of an intelligent and powerful Being. And if the fixed stars are the centers of other like systems . . . lest the systems of the fixed stars should, by their gravity, fall on each other mutually, he hath placed those systems at immense distances one from another." Having pointed out evidence of the Providence of God in the cosmos, Newton moved almost directly to the basic problem of showing the place of God in the vast new universe. His solution is to conceive of God as literally omnipresent:

> God . . . is eternal and infinite, omnipotent and omniscient; that is, his duration reaches from eternity to eternity; his presence from infinity to infinity. . . . He is not eternity or infinity, but eternal and infinite; he is not duration or space, but he endures and is present. He endures for ever, and is every where present; and by existing always and every where, he constitutes duration and space. . . . God is the same God, always and everywhere. He is omnipresent not *virtually* only, but also *substantially;* for virtue cannot exist without substance. In him are all things contained and moved; yet neither affects the other: God suffers nothing from the motion of bodies; bodies find no resistance from the omnipresence of God. It is allowed by all that the Supreme God exists necessarily; and by the same necessity he exists *always* and *every where.*

Omnipresence had of course been one of the basic attributes of God for many centuries. To the Middle Ages and Renaissance, however, it normally was an omnipresence that expressed itself from *without* rather than from *within* the physical universe.

It implies no diminution of Newton's great scientific achievements to note that to the average educated Englishman of the eighteenth century, these achievements apparently were valued less than the contributions which their author had made to theology, or, viewed historically, to the reunion of Christian theology and astronomy. In English poetry alone, hundreds of pages would be required to encompass the praise bestowed upon Newton as a "penman" for Deity. In lines representative of those composed by many other poets, Henry Brooke said in his description of Newton's *Principia:*

*Now had the Eternal Architect supreme,*
*In amplitude stretched out this wondrous frame,*
*Equipped magnificent the house of God,*
*Through height and depth his boundless blest abode!*
*One house, one world, one universe divine,*
*Where countless orbs through countless systems shine;*

*Systems, which viewed throughout the circuit wide,*
*Or lost, or scarce the pointed sight abide—*
*Through space immense with diminution seen,*
*Yet boundless all those worlds that roll within;*
*Each world as boundless to its native race,*
*That range and wanton through its ample space,*
*Frequent, through fields, through clouds of fragrance stray,*
*Or skim the watery or ethereal way. . . .*
  *Nature, bright effluence of the One Supreme!*
*O how connected is thy wondrous frame! . . .*
*Poised on Thy will the universal hung;*
*Attraction to its central magnet clung. . . .*
*Within, without, no second cause presides,*
*And One Sole Hand the mazed volution guides!*
*Hence endless good, hence endless order springs. . . .*

Some decades before the close of the eighteenth century, helio-centric astronomy had for much of educated Europe become an in-tegral part of a unified thought structure which included physics, philosophy, and theology. Particularly was this true of England. Its place was growing as secure and as important in this structure as had been that held by Aristotelian-Ptolemaic cosmology for many earlier centuries. A second cycle had been completed. For the Aristotelian-Ptolemaic-Biblical cosmology, the orthodox could now substitute the Copernican-Newtonian-(neo)Biblical universe.

To the humanist, the history of the three intermediate hypotheses is no less interesting and suggestive than that of the heliocentric. Taken purely as astronomical systems, none was so satisfactory and, in major outline, so beautifully simple as the Copernican theory. Yet the great majority of cosmologists who possessed in-itiative and intellectual courage turned first to the less radical hy-potheses.

We may note that by adoption of an intermediate hypothesis, its advocates kept more or less intact a structure of thought in which astronomy was a part. In general, these men went no further than they could go without endangering this structure. For the most part, they took no forward steps until their knowledge, frequently coupled with external pressure, compelled them to do so.

Approached from the vantage point of the systems themselves, rather than from that of their advocates, the evidence indicates that the intermediate hypothesis which best fitted the established pattern of thought (the geo-heliocentric) became the most important among this group. Scientifically, this hypothesis was of course inferior to the Fourth System.

Final scientific proof of the Copernican theory was not completed until Bessel's (and others') demonstration of annual stellar parallax in 1838, and Foucault's experimental demonstration of the earth's axial rotation with a pendulum in 1851. Among Protestants, including the educated public as well as the scientist, the Copernican theory and various of its amplifications had then been generally accepted for a century. Among Roman Catholics, the theory had had many advocates for a half-century. Quite obviously, other factors had proved more important than physical demonstrations.

The *Principia* of Newton naturally was one of these forces; the varied effects of time was another. With a majority of men, however, the most powerful single force was probably the successful incorporation of Copernican astronomy into a structure of thought whose values were more than scientific. It is not too much to suggest that, in numerous instances, intelligent men of the eighteenth century adopted the neo-Copernican system chiefly because of the values of the structure of which the system was a part. Without going too far afield by way of conclusion, we may speculate whether this aspect of the history of the Ptolemaic, Copernican, and Tychonic hypotheses has not again been duplicated in the field of international political theory.

# The Transition to
# Modern Science

*Walter Pagel*

# THE POSITION OF HARVEY
# AND VAN HELMONT IN THE HISTORY
# OF EUROPEAN THOUGHT*
## TO COMMEMORATE H. E. SIGERIST'S
## ESSAY ON HARVEY (1928)

It was 1928. The Weimar Republic could look back on certain important social and cultural successes achieved in the previous ten years against heavy odds in an atmosphere of party strife and hatred. Among its achievements was a new appreciation of the value of medical history. It was at this time that Sigerist reached his first climax as teacher and director of research at an institute that could take pride in a widely read yearbook and many other important publications of its own. At the same time a sister institute was created under the directorship of Paul Diepgen, and lecturerships and seminars sprang up in other places.

The same year, 1928, saw the three hundredth anniversary of the publication of Harvey's discovery of the circulation of the blood. Celebrations were held all over the globe. Here was an opportunity for physiologists to derive fresh inspiration for creative work from an historic book. This was the occasion of the first showing of a film which had been planned by the late Sir Thomas Lewis and produced by him in collaboration with Sir Henry Dale. It recorded

* Reprinted from *Journal of the History of Medicine and Allied Sciences,* Vol. XIII (1958), pp. 186-199, with the permission of the *Journal of the History of Medicine and Allied Sciences* and of the author.

demonstrations of many of Harvey's own experiments illustrating his argument, with a commentary of quotations from *De motu cordis*. Together with the new edition of 1957, produced in colour and with sound track, this film will surely be remembered at many Harvey anniversaries and centenaries yet to come.

A celebration quite different in character, yet also memorable, took place at Leipzig where on the foundation day of the University Sigerist delivered his oration on "Harvey's Position in the History of European Thought." [1] Like many of Sigerist's essays it is short. But it is weighty. Not that it contains the results of research leading to new data, facts, or scholarly detail; there is not a single quotation or footnote. Yet these ten pages are fraught with illuminating analyses of the situation from which—with Harvey—the scientific foundation of modern medicine arose. It is a complicated situation which under Sigerist's master hand is made transparent and easy to grasp. This pivots on the clear stipulation of what (and what alone) distinguishes Harvey from his predecessors. Various points had been raised in this connection, notably his departure from the teaching of the ancients, his advanced anatomical knowledge, and his method of putting observation and theory to the test of animal experiment. As Sigerist has shown, none of these points is essential. The decisive point is the employment, by Harvey, of calculation. Harvey computed, however roughly, the quantity of the blood driven from the heart in a given time and found that the volume of blood propelled in one hour exceeds that corresponding to the body weight by a factor of three. Where does this stupendous quantity of blood come from and where does it go? It certainly cannot be generated ever afresh, nor can it be absorbed at this rate by the tissues. There is no other way for the blood but to return to the heart via the veins in order to be driven out again by the arteries, in other words to circulate.

Harvey's argument from calculation had been related in full in

---

[1] Sigerist, H. E. William Harvey's Stellung in der europaeischen Geistesgeschichte. Rede gehalten an der Gruendungsfeier der Universität Leipzig. *Arch. Kulturgesch.*, 1929, *19*, 158-68.

presentations of his discovery, notably by Charles Singer.[2] It was Sigerist who drew attention to its significance as the turning point in the achievement of the discovery as such and its position in the history of medicine, science, and thought. "Here," Sigerist says, "an entirely new view of the facts emerges." Ancient theories were "qualitative," not "dynamic," in character. They were conceived without regard to movement and time. The Renaissance and humanism, intent on emulating and renewing the ancient ways, had abided by the ancient view. The result was fundamental to modern medicine too, but it had a "static" outlook corresponding to the mental climate from which it arose. Harvey's discovery marks the advent of the new epoch of Galileo and Sanctorius—the era of functional thinking brought about by the wide employment of computation, of measuring, and weighing.

In addition, Sigerist went one step farther. For this he derived inspiration from the history of art. Heinrich Woelfflin had demonstrated the new orientation in the fine arts which divided the era of "Baroque" in the second half of the 16th and the 17th centuries from the classicism of the Renaissance. The artist of the Baroque period dissolves the straight lines and planes—the "closed" forms of the Renaissance—in favour of movement, chiaroscuro, and depth. The Baroque master is no longer interested in "Being." He studies "Coming into Being"; in other words, he is concerned not with the limitations of objects, but with their infinite possibilites in movement and functon. Renaissance and Baroque thus represent two different ways of looking at nature; they embody two different views of the world.

Sigerist finds in Harvey the true exponent of the new Baroque spirit in biology and medicine, for his anatomy is "Anatomia Animata." Dissatisfied with the mere description of the heart, he integrates it with the functional laws which are obeyed by pulse and respiration. The same dynamic outlook is visible in his second great work—that on Generation. Harvey remains a "dynamist" in

[2] Singer, Charles. *The discovery of the circulation of the blood.* London, G. Bell, 1922, pp. 52 and 55.

all aspects of his creative work, and thus a true master of the Baroque period.

Sigerist's comments made a deep impression in wide circles at the time. Ever since they were propagated in Sigerist's lectures, seminars, and books, these stimulating ideas have been handed on to undergraduate and postgraduate students all over the world.

Today, just thirty years later, another Harveian centenary—the three hundredth anniversary of his death—is fresh in our minds. Sigerist did not survive to take part in it. It thus seems fitting to rediscuss his idea in the light of more recent historical research on Harvey and his discovery.

## II

Sigerist's idea is as fresh as ever and has proved its durability, at least in one respect. This concerns the line which divides Harvey from his predecessors. He discovered the closed circle described by the blood in its entirety, and the decisive new argument lay in the employment of computation. It was not the breakaway from ancient doctrines, as before him all those concerned with the demonstration of the true ways followed by the blood through the right heart and the lungs, had implicitly declared war on the ancient teaching. Nor was experimentalism the decisive step: Harvey's predecessors, notably Realdo Colombo and even Galen, had performed experiments. Nor was it finally the employment of reasoning from the basis of anatomical and observational data; in this way Cesalpino had gone a step farther than all other predecessors of Harvey in formulating and substantiating the "perpetual motion of blood from the veins into the heart and from the heart into the arteries." Moreover, Cesalpino must have been conscious of the import of his statement for he repeated it verbally and prominently during the next thirty years, between 1571, the year of the first edition of his "Peripatetic Questions," and 1603, the year of his death, and it appeared as well in posthumous editions.[3] There are further striking similarities in attitude between Cesalpino and Harvey, for example, the reverence accorded to Aristotle and to the preference given by the latter to the heart, the belief in the identity of venous and arterial blood, the stipulation that the lung merely refrigerates but does not add anything to the blood (such as air) and that "circulation" is comparable to "distillation" in achieving a refinement and "spiritualisation" of the blood.[4] Yet not far from the momentous statement quoted above we find a strange passage in the book of Cesalpino. Here he refers to Aristotle's doctrine that closure of the vein in the neck causes unconsciousness. He also tells us that Aristotle failed to distinguish clearly between arteries and veins, and that Galen had observed that closure of the artery in the neck has no such effect, whereas cutting of nerves has. Cesalpino explains that Galen's negative observation was due to the fact that even when the arterial blood supply to the brain was blocked, the latter still receives blood —through the veins which also carry "something from the heart to the brain." He resumes this speculation some twenty years later in his "Medical Questions" where he attributes sleep and unconsciousness to varying degrees of impairment in the supplying of blood to the brain by the veins. Even more surprisingly this is found in close

[3] Cesalpino, Andrea. *Quaestionum peripateticorum libri V*. Venice, 1593 (2d ed.; 1st ed., 1571), lib. V, quaest. 4, fol. 123 C: "Motus enim fit ex venis in cor caliditate alimentum trahente, simul autem ex corde in arterias, quia hac solum patet iter propter membranarum positionem: idem enim motus utraque oscula aperit venae scilicet in cor, cordis autem in arterias. . . ."

*Quaestionum medicarum libri II. Ibid.*, lib. II, quaest. 17, fol. 234 B: "sic enim perpetuus quidem motus est ex vena cava per cor et pulmones in arterian aortam: ut in quaestionibus peripateticis explicavimus."

*De plantis libri XVI* Florence 1583, lib. I, cap. 2, p. 3: "Nam in animalibus videmus alimentum per venas duci ad cor tanquam ad officinam caloris insiti et adepta inibi ultima perfectione per arterias in universum corpus distribui agente spiritu, qui ex eodem alimento in corde gignitur."

*Katoptron sive speculum artis medicae Hippocraticum*. Frankfurt, 1605, lib. 6, cap. 19, p. 472 (1st ed. Rome, 1601). The text is identical with: *Praxis universae artis medicae*. Treviso, 1606, lib. 6, cap. 19, p. 503: "ut continuus quidam motus fieret ex venis in Cor, et ex Corde in Arterias."

[4] For a detailed account see W. Pagel's William Harvey and the purpose of circulation. *Isis*, 1951, *42*, 22-38, notably pp. 23 *et seq*.

proximity to the view that the direction of the venous blood is centripetal towards the heart, as the experience of bloodletters shows, and as it should be to agree with Cesalpino's own teaching of the perpetual movement of blood to and from the heart.

The present author has attempted to explain this strange juxtaposition of what in the light of Harvey's discovery should be called "correct" and contradictory—"incorrect"—statements.[5] Here it may serve as an example to illustrate the advantage afforded by computation as employed by Harvey. Cesalpino lacks the certainty which Harvey could derive from calculation—the last and decisive test of his theory; it is thus that Cesalpino fails to arrive at the demonstration of a "closed" circulation of the blood.

## III

Harvey's discovery established modern physiology and thereby scientific medicine. It was the result of a modern method—that of analysis. Was Harvey a "Modern," then? He certainly was—if, by Harvey, we understand the discoverer of circulation and the critical observer of the developing chick. Just as certainly Harvey was not a "Modern," however, when we view his personality against the background of his work as a whole. Harvey follows the lead of Aristotelianism. The exalted position which he accorded to the heart, the "Sun of the Microcosm," is Aristotelian—just as much as is his principle that Nature does nothing in vain and that we must search for the final causes and purposes in physiology. The combination of reasoning and comparative anatomical observation, so fruitfully employed by Harvey, is typically Aristotelian too.

Sigerist himself pointed this out; but to him, Aristotelianism is the garb in which Harvey enters the literary stage and in which he appears as an Aristotelian *at first sight*.[6]

[5] Pagel, W. The philosophy of circles-Cesalpino-Harvey. A penultimate assessment. *J. Hist. Med.*, 1957, *12*, 140-57, notably pp. 146 *et seq.* with reference to *Quaest. peripatet.*, lib. V, quaest. 3, ed. 1593, fol. 121 D.

[6] "Harvey erscheint zunaechst durchaus als Aristoteliker," Sigerist, *loc. cit.*

Yet Harvey's adherence to Aristotle was more than that. It was thorough, sincere, and fundamental. Harvey was steeped in Aristotle. An outward sign is the close integration of the description of his discovery with Aristotelian quotations and peripatetic speculation. As Singer says: "It is very strange that in the midst of this, his great discovery, he should return again to the Aristotelian position. But so it is. He continues his reflections in words which might almost be quoted from Aristotle or rather from a mediaeval interpretation of Aristotle." [7]

Harvey was a man dedicated—not however to the aim of making a discovery or to the employment of modern methods or to the foundation of modern physiology, but to the solution of a *problem of purpose,* namely, that of circulation. Indeed, he was the "lifelong thinker" on the purpose of circulation.[8] This was the truly Aristotelian *Leitmotiv* of his investigation, and through it much can be explained in his life and work.

In Peripatetic Philosophy it was the purpose of circular processes to preserve and to regenerate. Thus the cosmos was "held together" by the circular movement of the celestial bodies. The same principle applied in Harvey's opinion to the circular movement of the blood, namely, the preservation of the body—the Microcosm— through a continual—circular—regeneration of the blood. Harvey found the same principle operative in generation—the repeated conversion of a shapeless particle of albumin into an organised body and back again to a shapeless particle—a cyclic process that serves the regeneration and preservation of the species.[9]

Indeed, Harvey paid no lip service to peripatetic thinking. It was no façade, but an integral part of the imposing building which he erected, a guide to observation as well as to speculation in comparative anatomy and embryology.

Yet Harvey's attitude to Aristotelianism was critical. He made frontal attacks on many a doctrine of the master. One example is

[7] Singer, *loc. cit.,* p. 56.
[8] Curtis, J. G. *Harvey's views on the use of the circulation of the blood.* New York, 1915, p. 152.
[9] See account and reference in Pagel, *loc. cit.* (n. 4), p. 29.

the seat of the soul which Harvey located in the blood—against the express depreciation of this view by Aristotle. It is in this critical attitude towards Aristotle also that Harvey perceptibly advances on his predecessors, notably Cesalpino. We mentioned above the strange juxtaposition of theories which seems to be due to Cesalpino's desire to support an Aristotelian doctrine even at the price of sacrificing his own correct idea of the venous blood flow. He may have been prepared to pay this price, but the juxtaposition of statements appearing contradictory today may not have impressed his original readers as such. Throughout his book Cesalpino does not make dogmatic statements but discusses and toys with various theories that are juxtaposed in order to be examined in the light of the Aristotelian tradition and also in that of reason and experience. On the whole, however, Cesalpino is less critical in his Aristotelian leanings and more intent on Aristotelian exegesis than Harvey. It is the peripatetic doctrine and its defence against Galen which forms the subject of his work, and, in this, naturalistic observation and judicious reasoning are employed as an aid to argument and exegesis. By contrast, Harvey's treatises are predominantly observational, and the support which his findings lend to the doctrines of Aristotle is an additional feature, however much satisfaction this provided for the author. Nevertheless, the true and genuine Aristotelianism which forged a strong link between Cesalpino and Harvey is all the more remarkable because it was actually Galen— whose knowledge of the blood flow by far exceeded that of Aristotle—who really provided the basis for discussion.

Temkin has rightly warned us against purging Harvey of "Aristotelian categories to make him appear a modern laboratory man pure and simple." [10] Today we easily separate Harvey's discovery from his Aristotelian and speculative learnings. Seen in historical perspective, however, they are inseparable.

[10] *Bull. Hist. Med.*, 1946, *19*, 26. See also Owsei Temkin's Metaphors of human biology. In: Stauffer, R. C. *Science and civilisation*. Madison, 1949, pp. 167-94, notably on Harvey, pp. 189 *et seq.*

**IV**

What, then, is Harvey's position as an exponent of the Baroque era? Here we must first admit the difficulties inherent in any attempt to define this period with reasonable distinctness. It is generally accepted to coincide with the Counter-Reformation, from the middle of the 16th century onwards. Michelangelo (1474-1563) is often regarded as the master who bridged the eras of the Renaissance and Baroque, but is usually claimed to represent the latter rather than the Renaissance. He was active in 1543 when anatomy, the typical product of the Renaissance spirit, reached its climax with the first appearance of Vesalius' great book. It is generally true that, as Shryock says, the 16th century was limited to a rebirth of classical medicine and that its "anatomical studies involved no new procedures and may be viewed as completing an ancient rather than as inaugurating a new tradition." [11] Looking at the illustrations of Vesalius, however, we soon perceive that some of them express movement. Moreover, the "modern"— "dynamic"—methods of measuring and weighing were first recommended in biology and medicine by Nicholas Cusanus (1401-64), one of the Platonists and humanists of the early Renaissance in the 15th century.

It follows that it is only in a broad sense that the term Baroque can be meaningful in medical history and can be accepted as a background for Harvey. We are inviting further difficulties, however, when we use it to indicate the departure towards modern science pure and simple—a science aloof from religious and philosophical speculation, i.e., from all nonscientific elements.

We have briefly dealt with the speculative—Aristotelian—element so closely bound up with the scientific revolution that was due to Harvey's work. It should be remembered that speculation

---

[11] Shryock, R. H., *National Tuberculosis Association 1904-1954. A study of the voluntary health movement in the United States.* New York, 1957, p. 3.

on Aristotelian lines is even recognisable in the works of Galileo. It would thus appear that the Baroque spirit fostered a strange co-existence of scientific with nonscientific elements—an attitude in which the latter in no way impeded, but rather supported, the inquiring mind.

Perhaps it is this interplay of opposites that reflects the Baroque spirit more faithfully than its identification with modern science pure and simple. The perspective of infinity achieved by the Baroque artist through the breaking up of straight lines, the interplay of light and shadow, and the representation of depth may indeed find its counterpart in the strange chiaroscuro of speculation and science displayed in the works of natural philosophers in the first half of the 17th century.

Understood in this sense we must include Joh. Baptista Van Helmont as an exponent of the period. In his case, not Aristotelian but religious and Neo-platonic speculation was intimately interwoven with progressive and quantitative work in science.

Calculation plays an integral part in the latter. As Partington says: "An important feature of Van Helmont's chemical work is its quantitative character: he made extensive use of the balance, expressed clearly the law of indestructibility of matter and emphasized that metals when dissolved in acids are not destroyed but can be recovered again by suitable means." [12] The present author would add that it was Van Helmont who implemented Nicolaus Cusanus' recommendation of weighing and measuring in biology and medicine on a large scale. His famous experiment with the willow tree is perhaps the best known example.[13] It was designed to prove the Biblical doctrine (later adopted by alchemists and Paracelsus) that all physical bodies consist in the last resort of water.[14] But Van

[12] Partington, J. R. Joan Baptista Van Helmont. *Ann. Sci.*, 1936, *1*, 359-84 (pp. 367-8).

[13] Complexionum atque mistionum elementalium figmentum. *Ortus medicinae*. Amsterdam, 1648 (1st ed.), cap. 20, p. 109. (1652, p. 88; 1707, p. 105.)

[14] This was based on Genesis I, 2: "And the Spirit of God moved upon the face of the Waters." As Raschi tells us of this passage, the conclusion had been drawn that water is older than earth. However, as Raschi emphasises

Helmont used the balance for practical purposes as well, for example, to determine the specific gravity of urine as an aid to diagnosis and prognosis.[15]

Examples of quantitative considerations from the work of Van Helmont could be multiplied. Only one more may be given—it concerns the discovery by which Van Helmont is chiefly remembered today, that of gas. Van Helmont's concept of gas embraces the modern—chemical and scientific—meaning, but in fact had a much wider purport. As we have seen, according to Van Helmont all objects are in the last resort water and therefore identical in their ultimate material composition. There is in each of them, however, an active principle, an "Archeus," that confers individual and species characteristics on them. This archeus is matter in a modified form. It is spiritualised and thereby enabled to receive the divine "forms" and "images." It is specifically organised matter, the material carrier of specificity in an object—its "gas." As such it is contained in the "semina" from which all objects develop. Normally invisible, it becomes demonstrable when the coarse material part of the object is removed. The royal road to this aim is combustion, hence Van Helmont's claim to the title of "Philosopher through Fire." The latter, to all appearances, destroys the object, but in reality converts it into a different gaseous form; the object itself remains there in its entirety. All that it loses is its original shape. Van Helmont says:

> . . . every coal although it be roasted even to its last day in a bright burning Furnace, the vessel being shut, it is fired indeed; but there is true fire in the Vessel, no otherwise than in the coal not being shut up; yet nothing of it is wasted, it not being able to be consumed, through the hindering of its efflux. Therefore the live coal, and generally whatsoever bodies do not immediately depart

---

in several places, it was not the intention of the Pentateuch to give a chronological account of creation—"eno mukdam um'uchar bathorah." Moreover, heaven consisted of watery as well as fiery material ("esh-majim" equals "hashamajim"—heaven).

[15] *Op. cit.* (n. 13), 1707, vol. II, p. 193, Deceptio 31: Scholarum humoristarum passiva. English tr., *Oriatrike* (Chandler), 1662, p. 1056.

into water, nor yet are fixed, do necessarily belch forth a wild spirit or breath. Suppose then, that of 62 pounds of Oaken coal, one pound of ashes is composed: Therefore the 61 remaining pounds are the wild spirit, which also being fired, cannot depart, the Vessel being shut. I call this Spirit, unknown hitherto, by the new name of Gas. . . . Bodies do contain this Spirit and do sometimes wholly depart into such a Spirit, not indeed because it is actually in those very bodies . . . but it is a Spirit grown together, coagulated after the manner of a body, and is stirred up by an attained ferment, as in Wine, the juyce of unripe grapes, bread, hydromel or water and honey. . . .[16]

Gas, therefore, is not contained *in* the object, but *is the object itself,* though devoid of its original shape. Unlike air and water vapour, gas is no volatile medium common to *all* things, but something *specific*. With this Van Helmont established a fundamental chemical conception and at the same time satisfied the main postulate of his own philosophy: that everything in Nature is determined by its specific organization. Pure matter—water—is separated from spirit by a deep gulf, matter endowed with specific organisation *is* spirit, though in a special "coagulated" form. Hence, spirit in turn is most subtle matter, carrying a specific seal. It is "gas." With this, Van Helmont has given—so it seemed—empirical proof of the existence of "Spiritual Bodies"—an article of the Christian Catechism, and provided a scientific basis for a monistic and pluralistic point of view replacing the unsatisfactory dualistic separation of spirit and body.[17]

[16] *Op. cit.* (n. 13), 1648, p. 106; 1652, p. 86; 1707, p. 102; 1662 (n. 15), p. 106. As Professor Partington pointed out in a personal communication to the present author (18 March 1942), a difficulty lies in the description of charcoal being transformed into gas on treating in a *closed* vessel. Certainly, Professor Partington says, "Gas cannot be kept in *any* vessel, open or *closed,* as the experiment with the closed bottle showed. This last is an important matter, as later workers had to find that gas *could* be kept in a vessel."

[17] See Pagel, W. The debt of science and medicine to a devout belief in God. Illustrated by the work of Van Helmont, *Tr. Victoria Inst.,* 1942, *74,* 99-115 (p. 106); *idem*. The religious and philosophical background of J. B. Van Helmont's science and medicine. *Bull. Hist. Med., Suppl.* 2, Baltimore, 1944, 44 pp. (p. 19).

Nothing could show more clearly the intimate blending of scientific and nonscientific motives, of discovery and speculation, that inspired the early 17th century "savant." It is recognisable in all provinces of Van Helmont's work, and we shall conclude with one more example: his discovery of acid gastric digestion. In this Van Helmont was preceded by Paracelsus who noticed the presence of the "hungry acid"—"Acetosum Esurinum"—in the stomach of those animals which were believed to digest metal and stone, for example, the ostrich. The same strong acid Paracelsus believed to be operative in spa water, notably of St. Moritz in the Engadin, accounting for its strengthening of appetite and digestion. He also credited spa water with protective and curative properties against the stone.[18] If it was the "hungry acid" that enabled the stomach of certain animals to dissolve stone and metal, what could be more obvious than that the action of spa water against the stone was due to this acid contained in it? This conclusion, formed in Paracelsus' treatise on "Diseases due to tartar," recurs in Van Helmont's work in a particularly interesting context which we shall discuss presently.

In his remarkable treatise on gastric digestion Van Helmont rejected the theory of Galen which attributed it to heat as well as that of Fernel which attributed it to an "Occult Virtue." He replaces these factors by a chemically defined substance—the "hungry acid" of Paracelsus. In contrast to the latter, who had still adhered to the "heat of digestion" and limited the action of acid to certain animals, Van Helmont clearly recognised its role in *all* animals and in man. He, therefore, remains the discoverer of acid gastric digestion.[19]

[18] Paracelsus. *Das Buch von den Tartarischen Krankheiten* (1537/38), Huser fol. ed., Strasburg, 1603, vol. I, p. 309.
[19] Calor efficienter non digerit sed tantum excitative. Heat does not digest efficiently but excitingly. *Op. cit.* (n. 13), 1648, pp. 201-6; 1652, pp. 161-5; 1707, pp. 192-7; 1662 (n. 15), pp. 198-203. German tr., *Auffgang der Arzneykunst,* Sulzbach, 1683, pp. 253-9. For an analysis of the treatise see Pagel, Van Helmont's ideas on gastric digestion and the gastric acid. *Bull. Hist. Med.,* 1956, *30,* 524-36. Before Van Helmont, in 1635, a little-known French Paracelsist, Fabius Violet, had referred to an "esprit dissoluant, qui fait les digestions (et non une chaleur simplement, ainsi que le suc de

Concerning the stone dissolving properties of the "hungry acid" Van Helmont says:

> Indeed, I have observed by experiment that a Pigeon did dissolve Duelech (the Stone) being cut out of man into a juyce, by the sharp ferment of her stomach, even as also the fragments of Bricks. . . . Yet this I have learned that the Spirit of Spanish salt, being distilled with the utmost fire of a *Reverbery*, together with Potters-earth, and being drunk every morning with white wine . . . takes away not onely the mortal stranguries of old people . . . but moreover the Stone . . . that it hath been at length diminished, and voyded out by pissing. . . . For thou hast the Balsame of Salt, which thou shalt never sufficiently esteem.[20]

As Partington has shown, Van Helmont describes in this passage "the distillation of spirit of sea-salt (*spiritus salis marini*), i.e., hydrochloric acid, from salt and dried potter's clay." [21] What inter-

---

limons, qui est froid, digere le perle aussi bien que l'esprit de vin qui est chaud)." This occurs in his book: *La parfaite et entière cognoissance de toutes les maladies du corps humain, causées par obstruction.* Paris, 1635, p. 142, with reference to the hungry acid (*Acetum esurinum*) which causes appetite and pain, if pathologically increased, owing to irritation of the stomach by "tartar." Thus, we have here already the rejection of the heat theory in favour of a "dissolving spirit" and in connection with the doctrine of "tartar" and stone. Violet assumes a position intermediate between Paracelsus and Van Helmont. It is difficult to say who formed his particular source of inspiration. It is noteworthy that Peter Severinus made gastric digestion depend upon the function and "properties" (*scientiae*) of "mechanical spirits" (i.e., salt, sulphur, and mercury), but he enlarges upon the pathogenic effects of acid, its causing pain and interfering with function everywhere in the body (*Idea medicinae philos.* Basel, 1571, p. 246 and 332). Nor had Croll anything relevant to say in his *Basilica chymica* of 1609. Nor finally is Van Helmont himself a possible source, although he had mentioned the "hungry acid" of Paracelsus and its preventive action against the stone in his "Supplement on the Waters of Spa" published in 1624. In Van Helmont's treatise on stone the stone-dissolving properties of the acid "ferment" of the pigeon's stomach as well as acid gastric digestion in general are discussed, but this treatise did not appear until 1644, i.e., four years prior to the publication of his *Opera* which contains the main treatise on gastric digestion.

[20] Ortus (n. 13), 1707, vol. II, p. 52: *De lithiasi,* VII, 28 (*Duelech resolutum*); 1662 (n. 15), p. 884.

[21] Partington, *loc. cit.* (n. 12), p. 382. Partington also dealt with another Helmontian preparation which, as he has shown, is not really a preparation

ests us is that this preparation of hydrochloric acid should occur in close proximity and conceptual connexion with a discussion of the virtues of the acid "ferment" of the pigeon's stomach. From this and other passages it would appear that Van Helmont came close to an identification of the acid "ferment" in the stomach with hydrochloric acid, although he does not seem to be fully conscious of this and it is by implication that we see him embarking on the correct way in this matter.

Again, Van Helmont's scientific exposition is bound up with nonscientific speculation. This leads us back to such mystical minds as Johann Reuchlin and Agrippa of Nettesheym,[22] and still farther back to the shady background of alchemy. Reuchlin, as well as Agrippa, rejected the heat theory of gastric digestion in favour of a divine "Occulta proprietas"—a specific factor. Digestion in their view is a "magic" effect. It accounts for the conversion of the food into body substance, an action comparable to that of the magnet or the attractive or protective effect of an amulet. Such magic effects are not explicable in terms of elemental or humoral mixture or astral virtues. It is from these sources that Fernel derived his doctrines in pathology in which he has little to offer that is original. Van Helmont presented his theory of acid gastric digestion in vitalistic terms. To him the acid is not itself the "vital ferment" that actually performs digestion, but it is acid that make its action possible. The "ferment" is an invisible spirit—an "image" of the

---

of hydrochloric acid. (See n. 13, 1707, p. 105. Partington quoted in detail both from the *Ortus* and the *Dageraed* on p. 371 of his paper.) He identified the nature of the gas produced in this experiment as chlorine and nitrosyl chloride (p. 374 of his paper under [vi]). In a personal communication to the author (8 Jan. 1958) Professor Partington emphasises that Van Helmont's "words 'distilla aquam' refer to the production of nitric acid (*aqua fortis*, etc.), as the starting materials show, and since sal ammoniac is added, chlorine and nitrosyl chloride would be developed, which (as usual) burst the vessel." The quotation of Partington's work relating to this experiment as given by the present author (see n. 19, p. 532) should be supplemented and read in the light of the above statements.

[22] Reuchlin, Johann. *De verbo mirifico,* II, 6. In: *Artis Cabalisticae . . . tomus I,* ed. Pistorius Niddanus. Basel, 1587, p. 912.—Agrippa, H. C. *De occulta philosophia.* Lugd., 1550, I, 10, p. 24.

process—i.e., a spiritual experience which displays physical effects. The professors of "Magia naturalis," notably Paracelsus and Agrippa, had attributed powerful magical effects to imagination which might even influence the stars.[23] In alchemical parlance, the "ferment" is a spiritual agent endowed with the power of "defeating" a substance by altering, converting, and transmuting it into something akin to the ferment itself. This is the power of the philosopher's stone whose action is "digestive"—"assimilating" a metal by bringing it back from its terminal, "fixed" state into a more "embryonic" form.[24] It is in this way that Van Helmont visualises gastric digestion: food is first reduced to a "middle life" by losing

[23] Magical thought and practices in the era of the Renaissance derive their fundamental inspiration from Marsilio Ficino. This has been brought out by the work of D. P. Walker (Spiritual and demonic magic. From Ficino to Campanella. London, Warburg Institute, 1958, pp. 85 et seq.) In this book the characteristic deviations of Agrippa's and Paracelsus' "demonic" magic from Ficino's "spiritual" (musical) magic are accorded particular attention. It remains to examine the influence of Ficino's ideas on biological and medical thought. In this respect the present author would refer in particular to the concept of Contagion—the well-known achievement of Fracastoro. The latter based his idea on the doctrine of sympathy and antipathy in nature. The same trend of thought, however, can be found in the work of Ficino on the Plague (1481) which antedates Fracastoro's treatise on Contagious Diseases (1546) by more than sixty years. Ficino says: "The more two persons are related to each other by birth, complexion, constitution or 'constellation,' the greater the danger of one being infected by the other. For infection is a transmutation of like into like—comparable to the resonance given by one of two guitars attuned to each other when the twin instrument is played." (De epidemiae morbo. Augsburg, 1518, sig. g iii, cap. XXII: De astantium conservatione qui infirmum regunt.) Perhaps the idea of "specific" (occult) properties so important in the thought of Reuchlin, Agrippa, and Paracelsus, has a basis in certain philosophical ideas connected with Ficino's doctrine of "Appetitus naturalis." As P. O. Kristeller formulates Ficino's idea: "Each thing, by virtue of its original quality has a peculiar tendency of its own which either excludes or at least surpasses in significance any other, arbitrary tendency." ". . . since natural movement is, so to speak, simply the external continuation of natural desire which originates directly in the nature of its bearer, the movement is no longer a condition communicated incidentally and from the outside, but the necessary emanation of its own inner substance and quality." "The nature of a thing is thus basically equivalent to its substance and coincides in the case of earthly creatures with the concept of species. Forces proceed from natures." (The philosophy of Marsilio Ficino. New York, Columbia University Press, 1943, pp. 171-5.)

[24] For some of the alchemical sources of the concept of "Fermentation" see Pagel (n. 19), pp. 533-4.

the terminal form in which it is found in nature and thereby made assimilable.

Our last example shows the depth of speculation in which a comparatively simple scientific discovery such as that of acid gastric digestion is embedded. We are inclined to regard this not as a single case but as typical of the period and indeed of the era of Baroque. In this, we would submit, lies the wisdom of Sigerist's concept which formed the basis of our discussion: Harvey's position in the history of European thought is determined by the peculiar spirit of his age, the age of a scientific revolution that is essentially bound up with nonscientific speculation, of the coexistence of contradictory tendencies, and of a dynamism that seems to burst through the limitations set to the human mind by ancient and Renaissance thought.

## ACKNOWLEDGMENT

The author is indebted to the Trustees of the Sir Henry S. Wellcome Trust for having enabled him to continue his research in medical history. He also wishes to thank Sir Henry Dale. O.M., G.B.E., F.R.S., Dr. F. H. K. Green, C.B.E., F.R.C.P., and Professor J. R. Partington for having revised the manuscript of the present paper.

*Gerald Holton*

# JOHANNES KEPLER'S UNIVERSE:
# ITS PHYSICS AND METAPHYSICS*

The important publications of Johannes Kepler (1571-1630) preceded those of Galileo, Descartes, and Newton in time, and in some
respects they are even more revealing. And yet, Kepler has been
strangely neglected and misunderstood. Very few of his voluminous writings have been translated into English.[1] In this language
there has been neither a full biography[2] nor even a major essay on
his work in over twenty years. Part of the reason lies in the apparent confusion of incongruous elements—physics and metaphysics,
astronomy and astrology, geometry and theology—which charac-
terizes Kepler's work. Even in comparison with Galileo and Newton, Kepler's writings are strikingly different in the *quality* of pre-

* Reprinted from *American Journal of Physics*, XXIV, 5 (1956), pp. 340-51,
with the permission of the *American Journal of Physics* and of the author.
The author's corrections of typographical errors in the original printing are
incorporated here.

[1] Books 4 and 5 of the *Epitome of Copernican Astronomy,* and Book 5 of
the *Harmonies of the World,* in *Great Books of the Western World* (Encyclopedia Britannica, Chicago, 1952), Vol. 16.
[2] The definitive biography is by the great Kepler scholar Max Caspar,
*Johannes Kepler* (W. Kohlhammer, Stuttgart, 1950); an English translation
is being prepared. [Published 1960; see Bibliography.—Ed.] A useful short
essay is in *Johann Kepler, 1571-1630* (edited by the History of Science
Society, Baltimore, 1931).

occupation. He is more evidently rooted in a time when animism, alchemy, astrology, numerology, and witchcraft presented problems to be seriously argued. His mode of presentation is equally uninviting to modern readers, so often does he seem to wander from the path leading to the important questions of physical science. Nor is this impression merely the result of the inevitable astigmatism of our historical hindsight. We are trained on the ascetic standards of presentation originating in Euclid, as reestablished for example in Books I and II of Newton's *Principia*,[3] and are taught to hide behind a rigorous structure the actual steps of discovery—those guesses, errors, and occasional strokes of good luck without which creative scientific work does not usually occur. But Kepler's embarrassing candor and intense emotional involvement force him to give us a detailed account of his tortuous progress. He still allows himself to be so overwhelmed by the beauty and variety of the world as a whole that he cannot yet persistently limit his attention to the main problems which can in fact be solved. He gives us lengthy accounts of his failures, though sometimes they are tinged with ill-concealed pride in the difficulty of his task. With rich imagination he frequently finds analogies from every phase of life, exalted or commonplace. He is apt to interrupt his scientific thoughts, either with exhortations to the reader to follow a little longer through the almost unreadable account, or with trivial side issues and textual quibbling, or with personal anecdotes or delighted exclamations about some new geometrical relation, a numerological or musical analogy. And sometimes he breaks into poetry or a prayer—indulging, as he puts it, in his "sacred ecstacy." We see him on his pioneering trek, probing for the firm ground on which our science could later build, and often led into regions which we now know to be unsuitable marshland.

These characteristics of Kepler's style are not merely idiosyn-

[3] But Newton's *Opticks*, particularly in the latter portions, is rather reminiscent of Kepler's style. In Book II, Part IV, Observation 5, there is, for example, an attempt to associate the parts of the light spectrum with the "Differences of the lengths of a monochord which sounds the tones in an eight."

crasies. They mirror the many-sided struggle attending the rise of modern science in the early 17th century. Conceptions which we might now regard as mutually exclusive are found to operate side-by-side in his intellectual make-up. A primary aim of this essay is to identify those disparate elements, and to show that in fact much of Kepler's strength stems from their juxtaposition. We shall see that when his physics fails, his metaphysics comes to the rescue; when a mechanical model breaks down as a tool of explanation, a mathematical model takes over, and at its boundary in turn there stands a theological axiom. Kepler set out to unify the classical picture of the world, one which was split into celestial and terrestrial regions, through the concept of a universal physical *force;* but when this problem did not yield to physical analysis, he readily returned to the devices of a unifying *image,* namely the central sun ruling the world, and of a unifying *principle,* that of all-pervading mathematical harmonies. In the end he failed in his initial project of providing the mechanical explanation for the observed motions of the planets; but he succeeded at least in throwing a bridge from the old view of the world as unchangeable *cosmos* to the new view of the world as the playground of dynamic and mathematical laws. And in the process he turned up, as if it were by accident, those clues which Newton needed for the eventual establishment of the new view.

## TOWARD A CELESTIAL MACHINE

*A sound instinct for physics and a commitment to neo-Platonic metaphysics*—these are Kepler's two main guides which are now to be examined separately and at their point of merger. As to the first, Kepler's genius in physics has often been overlooked by critics who were taken aback by his frequent excursions beyond the bounds of science as they came to be understood later, although his *Dioptrice* (1611) and his mathematical work on infinitesimals (in *Nova Stereometria,* 1615) and on logarithms (*Chilias Loga-*

*rithmorum,* 1624) have direct appeal for the modern mind. But even Kepler's casually delivered opinions often prove his insight beyond the general state of knowledge of his day. One example is his creditable treatment of the motion of projectiles on the rotating earth, equivalent to the formulation of the superposition principle of velocities (letter to David Fabricius, October 11, 1605). Another is his opinion of the *perpetuum mobile:*

> As to this matter, I believe one can prove with very good reasons that neither any never-ending motion nor the quadrature of the circle —two problems which have tortured great minds for ages—will ever be encountered or offered by nature.[4]

But of course, on a large scale, Kepler's genius lies in his early search for a physics of the solar system. He is the first to look for *a universal physical law based on terrestrial mechanics* to comprehend the whole universe in its quantitative details. In the Aristotelian and Ptolemaic world schemes, and indeed in Copernicus' own, the planets moved in their respective orbits by laws which were either purely mathematical or mechanical in a nonterrestrial sense. As Goldbeck reminds us,[5] Copernicus himself still warned to keep a clear distinction between celestial and merely terrestrial phenomena "so as not to attribute to the celestial bodies what belongs to the earth." This crucial distinction disappears in Kepler

[4] Letter to Herwart von Hohenburg, March 26, 1598, i.e., seven years before Stevinus implied the absurdity of perpetual motion in the *Hypomnemata Mathematica* (Leyden, 1605). Some of Kepler's most important letters are collected in Max Caspar and Walther von Dyck, *Johannes Kepler in seinen Briefen* (R. Oldenbourg, Munich and Berlin, 1930). A more complete collection in the original languages is to be found in Vols. 13-15 of the modern edition of Kepler's collected works, edited by W. von Dyke and M. Caspar (Beck, Munich, 1937 and later). In the past, these letters appear to have received insufficient attention in the study of Kepler's work and position. (The present English translations of all quotations from them are the writer's.) Excerpts from some letters were also translated by Carola Baumgardt, *Johannes Kepler* (Philosophical Library, Inc., New York, 1951).
[5] Ernst Goldbeck, "Abhandlungen zur Philosophie und ihrer Geschichte," in *Kepler's Lehre von der Gravitation* (Max Niemeyer, Halle, 1896), Vol. 6; a useful monograph demonstrating Kepler's role as a herald of mechanical astronomy. The reference is to *De Revolutionibus,* first edition, p. 3.

from the beginning. In his youthful work of 1596, the *Mysterium Cosmographicum,* a single geometrical device is used to show the necessity of the observed orbital arrangement of all planets. In this respect, the earth is treated as being an equal of the other planets.[6] In the words of Otto Bryk,[7]

> The central and permanent contribution lies in this, that for the first time the whole world structure was subjected to a single law of construction—though not a force law such as revealed by Newton, and only a noncausative relationship between spaces, but nevertheless one single law.

Four years later Kepler meets Tycho Brahe and from him learns to respect the power of precise observation. The merely approximate agreement between the observed astronomical facts and the scheme laid out in the *Mysterium Cosmographicum* is no longer satisfying. To be sure, Kepler always remained fond of this work, and in the *Dissertatio cum Nuncio Sidereo* (1610) even hoped that Galileo's newly-found moons of Jupiter would help to fill in one of the gaps left in his geometrical model. But with another part of his being Kepler knows that an entirely different approach is wanted. And here Kepler turns to the new conception of the universe. While working on the *Astronomia Nova,* Kepler lays out his program:

> I am much occupied with the investigation of the physical causes. My aim in this is to show that the celestial machine is to be likened

---

[6] In Kepler's Preface to his *Dioptrice* (1611) he calls his early *Mysterium Cosmographicum* "a sort of combination of astronomy and Euclid's Geometry," and describes the main features as follows: "I took the dimensions of the planetary orbits according to the astronomy of Copernicus, who makes the sun immobile in the center, and the earth movable both round the sun and upon its own axis; and I showed that the differences of their orbits corresponded to the five regular Pythagorean figures, which had been already distributed by their author among the elements of the world, though the attempt was admirable rather than happy or legitimate. . . ." The scheme of the five circumscribed regular bodies originally represented to Kepler the *cause* of the observed number (and orbits) of the planets: *"Habes rationem numeri planetarium."*

[7] Otto J. Bryk, translator and editor, *Johann Kepler, Die Zusammenklänge der Welten* (Diederichs, Jena, 1918), p. xxiii.

not to a divine organism but rather to a clockwork . . . , insofar as nearly all the manifold movements are carried out by means of a single, quite simple magnetic force, as in the case of a clockwork all motions [are caused] by a simple weight. Moreover I show how this physical conception is to be presented through calculation and geometry.[8]

The celestial machine, driven by a single terrestrial force, in the image of a clockwork! This is indeed a prophetic goal. Published in 1609, the *Astronomia Nova* significantly bears the subtitle *Physica Coelestis*. The book is best known for containing Kepler's First and Second Laws of planetary motion, but it represents primarily a search for one universal force law to explain the motions of planets —Mars in particular—as well as gravity and the tides. This breathtaking conception of unity is perhaps even more striking than Newton's, for the simple reason that Kepler had no predecessor.

THE PHYSICS OF THE CELESTIAL MACHINE

Kepler's first recognition is that forces between bodies are caused not by their relative positions or their geometrical arrangements, as was accepted by Aristotle, Ptolemy, and Copernicus, but by mechanical interactions between the material objects. Already in the *Mysterium Cosmographicum* (Chap. XVII) he announced *"Nullum punctum, nullum centrum grave est,"* and he gave the example of the attraction between a magnet and a piece of iron. In William Gilbert's *De Magnete* (1600), published four years later, Kepler finds a careful explanation that the action of magnets seems to come from pole points, but must be attributed to the parts of the body, not the points.

In the spirited "Objections" which Kepler appended to his own

---

[8] Letter to Herwart von Hohenburg, February 10, 1605. At about the same time he writes in a similar vein to Christian Severin Longomontanus concerning the relation of astronomy and physics: "I believe that both sciences are so closely interlinked that the one cannot attain completion without the other."

translation of Aristotle's Π ερὶ οὐρανοῦ, he states epigrammatically *"Das Mittele is nur ein Düpfflin,"* and he elaborates as follows:

> How can the earth, or its nature, notice, recognise and seek after the center of the world which is only a little point [Düpfflin]—and then go toward it? The earth is not a hawk, and the center of the world not a little bird; it [the center] is also not a magnet which could attract the earth, for it has no substance and therefore cannot exert a force.

In the Introduction to the *Astronomia Nova,* which we shall now consider in some detail, Kepler is quite explicit:

> A mathematical point, whether it be the center of the world or not, cannot move and attract a heavy object. . . . Let the [Aristotelian] physicists prove that such a force is to be associated with a point, one which is neither corporeal nor recognisable as anything but a pure reference [mark].

Thus what is needed is a "true doctrine concerning gravity"; the axioms leading to it include the following:

> Gravitation consists in the mutual bodily striving among related bodies toward union or connection; (of this order is also the magnetic force).

This premonition of universal gravitation is by no means an isolated example of lucky intuition. Kepler's feeling for the physical situation is admirably sound, as shown in additional axioms:

> If the earth were not round, a heavy body would be driven not everywhere straight toward the middle of the earth, but toward different points from different places.
>
> If one were to transport two stones to any arbitrary place in the world, closely together but outside the field of force [*extra orbe virtutis*] of a third related body, then those stones would come together at some intermediate place similar to two magnetic bodies, the first approaching the second through a distance which is proportional to the mass [*moles*] of the second.

And after this precursor of the principle of conservation of momentum, there follows the first attempt at a good explanation for the tides in terms of a force of attraction exerted by the moon.

But the Achilles heel of Kepler's celestial physics is found in the very first "axiom," in his Aristotelian conception of the law of inertia, where inertia is identified with a tendency to come to rest—*causa privativa motus:*

> Outside the field of force of another related body, every bodily substance, insofar as it is corporeal, by nature tends to remain at the same place at which it finds itself.[9]

This axiom deprives him of the concepts of mass and force in useful form—the crucial tools needed for shaping the celestial metaphysics of the ancients into the celestial physics of the moderns. Without these concepts, Kepler's world machine is doomed. He has to provide separate forces for the propulsion of planets tangentially along their paths and for the radial component of motion.

Moreover, he assumed that the force which reaches out from the sun to keep the planets in tangential motion falls inversely with the increasing distance. The origin and the consequences of this assumption are very interesting. In Chap. 20 of the *Mysterium Cosmographicum,* he speculated casually why the sidereal periods of revolution on the Copernican hypothesis should be larger for the more distant planets, and what force law might account for this:

> We must make one of two assumptions: either the forces of motion [*animae motrices*] [are inherent in the planets] and are feebler the more remote they are from the sun, or there is only one *anima motrix* at the center of the orbits, that is, in the sun. It drives the more vehemently the closer the [moved] body lies; its effect on the more distant bodies is reduced because of the distance [and the

[9] Previously, Kepler discussed the attraction of the moon in a letter to Herwart, January 2, 1607. The relative motion of two isolated objects and the concept of inertia are treated in a letter to D. Fabricius, October 11, 1605. On the last subject, see A. Koyré, Phil. Rev. 52, 344-345 (1943).

corresponding] decrease of the impulse. Just as the sun contains the source of light and the center of the orbits, even so can one trace back to this same sun life, motion and the soul of the world. . . . Now let us note how this decrease occurs. To this end we will assume, as is very probable, that the moving effect is weakened through spreading from the sun in the same manner as light.

This suggestive image—with its important overtones which we shall discuss below—does, however, not lead Kepler to the inverse-square law of force, for he is thinking of the spreading of light *in a plane,* corresponding to the plane of planetary orbits. The decrease of light intensity is therefore associated with the linear increase in circumference for more distant orbits! In his pre-Newtonian physics, where force is proportional not to acceleration but to velocity, Kepler finds a ready use for the inverse first-power law of gravitation. It is exactly what he needs to explain his observation that the speed of a planet in its elliptical orbit decreases linearly with the increase of the planet's distance from the sun. Thus Kepler's Second Law of Planetary Motion—which he actually discovered *before* the so-called First and Third laws—finds a partial physical explanation in joining several erroneous postulates.

In fact, it is clear from the context that these postulates originally suggested the Second Law to Kepler.[10] But not always is the final outcome so happy. Indeed, the hypothesis concerning the physical forces acting on the planet seriously delays Kepler's progress toward the law of elliptical orbits (First Law). Having shown that "the path of the planet [Mars] is not a circle but an oval figure," he attempts (Chap. 45, *Astronomia Nova*) to find the details of a physical force law which would explain the "oval" path in a quan-

[10] Not only the postulates but also some of the details of their use in the argument were erroneous. For a short discussion of this concrete illustration of Kepler's use of physics in astronomy, see J. L. E. Dreyer, *History of the Planetary System from Thales to Kepler* (Dover Publications, New York, 1953), second edition, pp. 387-399. A longer discussion is in Max Caspar's introductory material to his edition of the *Astronomia Nova* (R. Oldenbourg, Munich and Berlin, 1929).

titative manner. But after ten chapters of tedious work he has to confess that "the physical causes in the 45th chapter thus go up in smoke." Then in the remarkable 57th chapter, a final and rather desperate attempt is made to formulate a force law. Kepler even dares to entertain the notion of combined magnetic influences and animal forces (*via animali*) in the planetary system. Of course, the attempt fails. The accurate clockwork-like celestial machine cannot be constructed.

To be sure, Kepler does not give up his conviction that a universal force exists in the universe, akin to magnetism. For example, in Book 4 of the *Epitome of Copernican Astronomy* (1620), we encounter the picture of the sun as a spherical magnet with one pole at the center and the other distributed over its surface. Thus a planet, itself magnetized like a bar magnet with a fixed axis, is alternately attracted to and repelled from the sun in its elliptical orbit. This is to explain the radial component of planetary motion. The tangential motion has been previously explained (in Chap. 34, *Astronomia Nova*) as resulting from the drag or torque which magnetic lines of force from the rotating sun are supposed to exert on the planet as they sweep over it. But the picture remains qualitative and incomplete, and Kepler does not return to his original plan to "show how this physical conception is to be presented through calculation and geometry." [8] Nor does his long labor bring him even a fair amount of recognition. Galileo introduces Kepler's work into his discussion on the world systems only to scoff at Kepler's notion that the moon affects the tides,[11] even though Tycho Brahe's data and Kepler's work based on them had shown that the Copernican scheme which Galileo was so ardently upholding did not correspond to the experimental facts of planetary motion. And Newton manages to remain strangely silent about Kepler throughout Books I and II of the *Principia,* by introducing the Third Law anony-

[11] *Dialogue on the Great World Systems,* edited by Giorgio de Santillana (University of Chicago Press, Chicago, 1953), p. 469. However, an oblique compliment to Kepler's Third Law may be intended in a passage on p. 286.

mously as "the phenomenon of the $\frac{3}{2}$th power" and the First and Second Laws as "the *Copernican* hypothesis." [12] Kepler's three laws have come to be treated as essentially empirical rules. How far removed this achievement was from his original ambition!

### KEPLER'S FIRST CRITERION OF REALITY: THE PHYSICAL OPERATIONS OF NATURE

Let us now set aside for a moment the fact that Kepler failed to build a mechanical model of the universe, and ask why he undertook the task at all. The answer is that Kepler (rather like Galileo) was trying to establish a new philosophical interpretation for "reality." Moreover, he was quite aware of the novelty and difficulty of the task.

In his own words, Kepler wanted to "provide a philosophy or physics of celestial phenomena in place of the theology or metaphysics of Aristotle." [13] Kepler's contemporaries generally regarded his intention of putting laws of physics into astronomy as a new and probably pointless idea. Even Michael Mästlin, Kepler's own beloved teacher, who had introduced Kepler to the Copernican theory, wrote him:

[12] *Principia,* edited by F. Cajori (University of California Press, Berkeley, 1946), pp. 394-395. In Book III, Newton remarks concerning the fact that the Third Law applies to the moons of Jupiter: "This we know from astronomical observations." At last, on page 404, Kepler is credited with having "first observed" that the $\frac{3}{2}$ power law applies to the "five primary planets" and the earth. Newton's real debt to Kepler was best summarized in his own letter to Halley, July 14, 1686: "But for the duplicate proportion [the inverse-square law of gravitation] I can affirm that I gathered it from Kepler's theorem about twenty years ago."

[13] Letter to Johann Brengger, October 4, 1607. This picture of a man struggling to emerge from the largely Aristotelian tradition is perhaps as significant as the usual one of Kepler as Copernican in a Ptolemaic world. Nor was Kepler's opposition, strictly speaking, Ptolemaic any longer. For this we have Kepler's own opinion (*Harmonice Mundi,* Book 3): "First of all, readers should take it for granted that among astronomers it is nowadays agreed that all planets circulate around the sun . . . ," meaning of course the system not of Copernicus but of Tycho Brahe, in which the earth was fixed and the moving sun served as center of motion for the other planets.

Concerning the motion of the moon you write you have traced all the inequalities to physical causes; I do not quite understand this. I think rather that here one should leave physical causes out of account, and should explain astronomical matters only according to astronomical method with the aid of astronomical, not physical, causes and hypotheses. That is, the calculation demands astronomical bases in the field of geometry and arithmetic. . . .[14]

The difference between Kepler's conception of the "physical" problems of astronomy and the methodology of his contemporaries reveals itself clearly in the juxtaposition of representative letters by the two greatest astronomers of the time—Tycho Brahe and Kepler himself. Tycho, writing to Kepler (December 9, 1599) repeats the preoccupation of two millenia of astronomical speculations:

I do not deny that the celestial motions achieve a certain symmetry [through the Copernican hypothesis], and that there are reasons why the planets carry through their revolutions around this or that center at different distances from the earth or the sun. However, the harmony or regularity of the scheme is to be discovered only *a posteriori*. . . . And even if it should appear to some puzzled and rash fellow that the superposed circular movements on the heavens yield sometimes angular or other figures, mostly elongated ones, then it happens accidently, and reason recoils in horror from this assumption. For one must compose the revolutions of celestial objects definitely from circular motions; otherwise they could not come back on the same path eternally in equal manner, and an eternal duration would be impossible, not to mention that the orbits would be less simple, and irregular, and unsuitable for scientific treatment.

This manifesto of ancient astronomy might indeed have been subscribed to by Pythagoras, Plato, Aristotle, and Copernicus himself. Against it, Kepler maintains a new stand. Writing to D. Fabricius (August 1, 1607), he sounds the great new *leitmotif* of astronomy: *"The difference consists only in this, that you use circles, I use bodily forces."* And in the same letter, he defends his use of the

[14] Letter of October 1, 1616.

ellipse in place of the superposition of circles to represent the orbit of Mars:

> When you say it is not to be doubted that all motions occur on a perfect circle, then this is false for the composite, i.e., the real motions. According to Copernicus, as explained, they occur on an orbit distended at the sides, whereas according to Ptolemy and Brahe on spirals. But if you speak of components of motion, then you speak of something existing in thought, i.e., something that is not there in reality. For nothing courses on the heavens except the planetary bodies themselves—no orbs, no epicycles. . . .

This straightforward and modern-sounding statement implies that behind the word "real" stands "mechanical," that for Kepler the real world is the world of objects and of their mechanical interactions in the sense which Newton used, e.g., in the preface to the *Principia*:

> Then from these [gravitational] forces, by other propositions which are also mathematical, I deduce the motions of the planets, the comets, the moon, and the sea. I wish we could derive the rest of the phenomena of nature by the same kind of reasoning from mechanical principles. . . .[15]

Thus we are tempted to see Kepler as a natural philosopher of the mechanistic-type later identified with the Newtonian disciples. But this is deceptive. Particularly after the failure of the program of the *Astronomia Nova,* another aspect of Kepler asserted itself. Though he does not appear to have been conscious of it, he never resolved finally whether the criteria of reality are to be sought on the *physical* or the *metaphysical* level. The words "real" or "physical" themselves, as used by Kepler, carry two interpenetrating complexes of meaning. Thus on receiving Mästlin's letter[14] of October 1, 1616, Kepler jots down in the margin his own definition of "physical":

[15] See reference 12, p. xviii.

I call my hypotheses physical for two reasons. . . . My aim is to assume only those things of which I do not doubt they are real and consequently physical, where one must refer to the nature of the heavens, not the elements. When I dismiss the perfect excentric and the epicycle, I do so because they are purely geometrical assumptions, for which a corresponding body in the heavens does not exist. The second reason for my calling my hypotheses physical is this . . . I prove that the irregularity of the motion [of planets] corresponds to the nature of the planetary sphere, i.e., is physical.

This throws the burden on the *nature* of heavens, the *nature* of bodies. How, then, is one to recognize whether a postulate or conception is in accord with the nature of things?

This is the main question, and to it Kepler has at the same time two very different answers, emerging, as it were, from the two parts of his soul. We may phrase one of the two answers as follows: *The physically real world, which defines the nature of things, is the world of phenomena explainable by mechanical principles.* This can be called Kepler's first criterion of reality, and assumes the possibility of formulating a sweeping and consistent dynamics which Kepler only sensed but which was not to be given until Newton's *Principia.* Kepler's other answer, to which he keeps returning again and again as he finds himself rebuffed by the deficiencies of his dynamics, and which we shall now examine in detail, is this: *The physically real world is the world of mathematically expressed harmonies which man can discover in the chaos of events.*

KEPLER'S SECOND CRITERION OF REALITY: THE
MATHEMATICAL HARMONIES OF NATURE

Kepler's failure to construct a *Physica Coelestis* did not damage his conception of the astronomical world. This would be strange indeed in a man of his stamp if he did not have a ready alternative to the mechanistic point of view. Only rarely does he seem to have been really uncomfortable about the poor success of the latter, as when he is forced to speculate how a soul or an inherent intelligence would help to keep a planet on its path. Or again, when the period of rotation of the sun which Kepler had postulated in his physical model proved to be very different from the actual rotation as first observed through the motion of sunspots, Kepler was characteristically not unduly disturbed. The truth is that despite his protestations, Kepler was not as committed to mechanical explanations of celestial phenomena as was, say, Newton. He had another route open to him.

His other criterion, his second answer to the problem of physical reality, stemmed from the same source as his original interest in astronomy and his fascination with a universe describable in mathematical terms, namely from a frequently acknowledged metaphysics rooted in Plato and neo-Platonists such as Proclus Diadochus. It is the criterion of *harmonious regularity in the descriptive laws of science*. One must be careful not to dismiss it either as just a reappearance of an old doctrine or as an aesthetic requirement which is still recognized in modern scientific work; Kepler's conception of what is "harmonious" was far more sweeping and important than either.

A concrete example is again afforded by the Second Law, the "Law of Equal Areas." To Tycho, Copernicus, and the great Greek astronomers, the harmonious regularity of planetary behavior was to be found in the uniform motion in component circles. But Kepler recognized the orbits—after a long struggle—as ellipsi on which planets move in a nonuniform manner. The figure is lopsided. The speed varies from point to point. And yet, nestled within this double complexity is hidden a harmonious regularity which transports its ecstatic discoverer—namely the fact that a constant area is swept out in equal intervals by a line from the focus of the ellipse, where the sun is, to the planet on the ellipse. For Kepler, the law is harmonious in three separate senses.

First, *it is in accord with experience*. Whereas Kepler, despite long and hard labors, had been unable to fit Tycho's accurate observations on the motion of Mars into a classical scheme of superposed circles, the postulate of an elliptical path fitted the observations at once. Kepler's dictum was: "harmonies must accommodate experience." [16] How difficult it must have been for Kepler, a Pythagorean to the marrow of his bones, to forsake circles for ellipsi! For a mature scientist to find in his own work the need for abandoning his cherished and ingrained preconceptions, the very basis of his previous scientific work, in order to fulfill the dictates of quantitative experience—this was perhaps one of the great sacrificial acts of modern science, equivalent in recent scientific history to the agony of Max Planck. Kepler clearly drew the strength for this act from the belief that it would help him to gain an even deeper insight into the harmony of the world.

The second reason for regarding the law as harmonious is its reference to, or discovery of, a *constancy*—although no longer a constancy simply of angular velocity but of areal velocity. The typical law of ancient physical science had been Archimedes' law of the lever: a relation of direct observables in static configuration. Even the world systems of Copernicus and of Kepler's *Mysterium Cosmographicum* still had lent themselves to visualization in terms of a set of fixed concentric spheres. And we recall that Galileo never made use of Kepler's ellipsi, but remained to the end a true follower of Copernicus who had said "the mind shudders" at the supposition of noncircular nonuniform celestial motion, and "it would be unworthy to suppose such a thing in a Creation constituted in the best possible way."

With Kepler's First Law and the postulation of elliptical orbits, the old simplicity was destroyed. The Second and Third Laws established the physical law of constancy as an ordering principle in a changing situation. Like the concepts of momentum and caloric in later laws of constancy, areal velocity itself is a concept far removed from the immediate observables. It was therefore a bold step to search for harmonies beyond both perception and preconception.

[16] Quoted in *Weltharmonik,* edited by Max Caspar (R. Oldenbourg, Munich and Berlin, 1939), p. 55 *.

Thirdly, the law is harmonious also in a grandiose sense: the fixed point of reference in the law of equal areas, the "center" of planetary motion, is the center of the *sun itself,* whereas even in the Copernican scheme the sun was a little off the center of planetary orbits. With this discovery Kepler makes the planetary system at last truly heliocentric, and thereby satisfies his instinctive and sound demand for some material object as the "center" to which ultimately the physical effects that keep the system in orderly motion must be traced.

For Kepler, the last of these three points is particularly exciting. The sun at its fixed and commanding position at the center of the planetary system matches the picture which always rises behind Kepler's tables of tedious data—the picture of a centripetal universe, directed toward and guided by the *sun* in its manifold roles: as the *mathematical* center in the description of celestial motions; as the central *physical* agency for assuring continued motion; and above all as the *metaphysical* center, the temple of the Deity. The three roles are in fact inseparable. For granting the special simplicity achieved in the description of planetary motions in the heliocentric system, as even Tycho was willing to grant, and assuming also that each planet must experience a force to drag it along its own constant and eternal orbit, as Kepler no less than the Scholastics thought to be the case, then it follows that the common need is supplied from what is common to all orbits, i.e., their common center; and this source of eternal constancy itself must be constant and eternal. Those however, are precisely the unique attributes of the Deity.

Using his characteristic method of reasoning on the basis of archetypes, Kepler piles further consequences and analogies on this argument. The most famous is the comparison of the world-sphere with the Trinity: the sun, being at the center of the sphere and thereby antecedent to its two other attributes, namely surface and volume, is compared to God the Father. With variations the analogy occurs many times throughout Kepler's writings, including many of his letters. The image haunts him from the very beginning (e.g., Chap. II, *Mysterium Cosmographicum*) and to the very end. Clearly, it is not sufficient to dismiss it with the usual phrase "sun-worship." [17] At the very least, one would have to allow that the exuberant Kepler is a worshipper of the whole solar system in all its parts.

The power of the sun-image can be traced to the acknowledged influence on Kepler by neo-Platonists such as Proclus (5th century) and Witelo (13th century). At the time it was current neo-Platonic doctrine to identify light with "the source of all existence" and to hold that "space and light are one." [18] Indeed, one of the main preoccupations of the 16th century neo-Platonists had been, to use a modern term, the transformation properties of space, light, and soul. Kepler's discovery of a truly heliocentric system is not only in perfect accord with the conception of the sun as a ruling entity, but allows him, for the first time, to focus attention on the sun's position through argument from physics.

In the medieval period the "place" for God, both in Aristotelian and in neo-Platonic astronomical metaphysics, had commonly been either beyond the last celestial sphere or else all of space; for only those alternatives provided for the Deity a "place" from which all celestial motions were equivalent. But Kepler can adopt a third possibility: in a truly heliocentric system God can be brought back into the solar system itself, so to speak, enthroned at the fixed and common reference object which coincides with the source of light and with the origin of the physical forces holding the system together. In the *De Revolutionibus* Copernicus had glimpsed part of this image when he wrote, after describing the planetary arrangement,

[17] E.g., E. A. Burtt, *The Metaphysical Foundations of Modern Science* (Routledge and Kegan Paul, London, 1932), p. 47 ff.
[18] For a recent analysis of neo-Platonic doctrine, which regrettably omits a detailed study of Kepler, see Max Jammer, *Concepts of Space* (Harvard University Press, Cambridge, 1954), p. 37 ff. Neo-Platonism in relation to Kepler is discussed by Thomas Kuhn, *The Copernican Revolution: Planetary Astronomy in Western Thought* (in preparation). [Published by Harvard University Press, 1957; reprinted by Modern Library, 1959.—Ed.]

In the midst of all, the sun reposes, unmoving. Who, indeed, in this most beautiful temple would place the light-giver in any other part than that whence it can illumine all other parts?

But Copernicus and Kepler were quite aware that the Copernican sun was not quite "in the midst of all"; hence Kepler's delight when, as one of his earliest discoveries, he found that the orbital planes of all planets intersect at the sun.

The threefold implication of the heliocentric image as mathematical, physical, and metaphysical center helps to explain the spell it casts on Kepler. As Wolfgang Pauli has pointed out in a highly interesting discussion of Kepler's work as a case study in "the origin and development of scientific concepts and theories," here lies the motivating clue: "It is because he sees the sun and planets against the background of this fundamental image [archetypische Bild] that he believes in the heliocentric system with religious fervor"; it is this belief "which causes him to search for the true laws concerning the proportion in planetary motion. . . ." [19]

To make the point succinctly, we may say that in its final version *Kepler's physics of the heavens is heliocentric in its kinematics, but theocentric in its dynamics,* where harmonies based in part on the properties of the Deity serve to supplement physical laws based on the concept of specific quantitative forces. This brand of physics is most prominent in Kepler's last great work, the *Harmonice Mundi* (1619). There the so-called Third Law of planetary motion is announced without any attempt to deduce it from mechanical principles, whereas in the *Astronomia Nova* magnetic forces had driven —no, obsessed—the planets. As in his earliest work, he shows that the phenomena of nature exhibit underlying mathematical harmonies. Having not quite found the mechanical gears of the world machine, he can at least give its equations of motion.

[19] W. Pauli, "Der Einfluss archetypischer Vorstellungen auf die Bildung naturwissenschaftlicher Theorien bei Kepler," in *Naturerklärung und Psyche,* C. G. Jung and W. Pauli (Rascher, Zürich, 1952), p. 129. A pending English translation of the book has been announced by Pantheon Press under the title *The Interpretation of Nature and the Psyche.* [Published 1955.—Ed.]

THE SOURCE OF KEPLER'S HARMONIES

Unable to identify Kepler's work in astronomy with physical science in the modern sense, many have been tempted to place him on the other side of the imaginary dividing line between classical and modern science. Is it after all, such a large step from the harmonies which the ancients found in circular motion and rational numbers to the harmonies which Kepler found in elliptical motions and exponential proportions? Is it not merely a generalization of an established point of view? Both answers are in the negative. For the ancients and for most of Kepler's contemporaries, the hand of the Deity was revealed in nature through laws which, if not qualitative, were harmonious in an essentially self-evident way; the axiomatic simplicity of circles and spheres and integers itself proved their deistic connection. But Kepler's harmonies reside in the very fact that the relations *are quantitative,* not in some specific simple *form* of the quantitative relations.

*It is exactly this shift which we can now recognize as one point of breakthrough toward the later, modern conception of mathematical law in science.* Where in classical thought the quantitative actions of nature were limited by a few necessities, the new attitude, whatever its metaphysical motivation, opens the imagination to an infinity of possibilities. As a direct consequence, where in classical thought the quantitative results of experience were used largely to fill out a specific pattern by *a priori* necessity, the new attitude permits the results of experience to reveal in themselves whatever pattern nature has in fact chosen from the infinite set of possibilities. Thus the seed is planted for the general view of most modern scientists, who find the world harmonious in a vague aesthetic sense because the mind can find, inherent in the chaos of events, order framed in mathematical laws—of whatever form they may be. As has been aptly said about Kepler's work:

Harmony resides no longer in numbers which can be gained from arithmetic without observation. Harmony is also no longer the property of the circle in higher measure than the ellipse. Harmony is present when a multitude of phenomena is regulated by the unity of a mathematical law which expresses a cosmic idea.[20]

Perhaps it was inevitable in the progress of modern science that the harmony of mathematical law should now be sought in aesthetics rather than in metaphysics. But Kepler himself would have been the last to propose or accept such a generalization. The ground on which he postulated that harmonies reside in the quantitative properties of nature lies in the same metaphysics which helped him over the failure of his physical dynamics of the solar system. Indeed, the source is as old as natural philosophy itself: *the association of quantity per se with Deity.* Moreover, as we can now show, Kepler held that man's ability to discover harmonies, and therefore reality, in the chaos of events is due to a direct connection between ultimate reality, namely God, and the mind of man.

In an early letter, Kepler opens to our view this main spring of his life's work:

May God make it come to pass that my delightful speculation [the *Mysterium Cosmographicum*] have everywhere among reasonable men fully the effect which I strove to obtain in the publication, namely that the belief in the creation of the world be fortified through this external support, that thought of the creator be recognized in its nature, and that his inexhaustible wisdom shine forth daily more brightly. Then man will at last measure the power of his mind on the true scale, and will realize that *God, who founded everything in the world according to the norm of quantity, also has endowed man with a mind which can comprehend these norms.* For as the eye for color, the ear for musical sounds, so is the mind of man created for the perception not of any arbitrary entities, but rather of quantities; the mind comprehends a thing the more cor-

[20] H. Zaiser, *Kepler als Philosoph* (E. Surkamp, Stuttgart, 1932), p. 47.

rectly the closer the thing approaches toward pure quantity as its origin.[21]

On a superficial level, one may read this as another repetition of the old Platonic principle ὁ ϑεὸς ἀεὶ γεωμετρεῖ; and of course Kepler does believe in "the creator, the true first cause of geometry, who, as Plato says, always geometrizes" (*Harmonice Mundi,* Book 3). Kepler is indeed a Platonist, and even one who is related at the same time to both neo-Platonic traditions—which one might perhaps better identify as the neo-Platonic and the neo-Pythagorean—, that of the mathematical physicists like Galileo, and that of the mathematical mysticism of the Florentine Academy. But Kepler's God has done more than build the world on a mathematical model; he has also specifically created man with a mind which "carries in it concepts built on the category of quantity," [21]—*in order that man may directly communicate with the Deity:*

> Those laws [which govern the material world] lie within the power of understanding of the human mind; God wanted us to perceive them when he created us in His image in order that we may take part in His own thoughts. . . . Our knowledge [of numbers and quantities] is of the same kind as God's, at least insofar as we can understand something of it in this mortal life.[22]

[21] Letter to Mästlin, April 19, 1597. (Italics supplied.) The "numerological" component of modern physical theory is in fact a respectable offspring from this respectable antecedent. For example, see Niels Bohr, *Atomic Theory and the Description of Nature* (The Macmillan Company, New York, 1934), pp. 103-104: "This interpretation of the atomic number [as the number of orbital electrons] may be said to signify an important step toward the solution of one of the boldest dreams of natural science, namely, to build up an understanding of the regularities of nature upon the consideration of pure number."

[22] Letter to Herwart, April 9/10, 1599. Galileo later expressed the same principle: "That the Pythagoreans had the science of numbers in high esteem, and that Plato himself admired human understanding and thought that it partook of divinity, in that it understood the nature of numbers, I know very well, nor should I be far from being of the same opinion." *Dialogue on the Great World Systems,* p. 14. Descartes' remark "You can substitute the mathematical order of nature for 'God' whenever I use the latter term" stems from the same source.

The procedure by which one apprehends harmonies is described quite explicitly in Book 4, Chapter 1 of *Harmonice Mundi*. There are two kinds of harmonies, namely those in sense phenomena, as in music, and in "pure" harmonies such as are "constructed of mathematical concepts." The feeling of harmony arises when there occurs a matching of the perceived order with the corresponding innate archetype (*archetypus, Urbild*). The archetype itself is part of the mind of God, and was impressed on the human soul by the Deity when He created man in His image. The kinship with Plato's doctrine of ideal forms is clear. But whereas the latter, in the usual interpretation, are to be sought outside the human soul, Kepler's archetypes are within the soul. As he summarizes at the end of the discussion, the soul carries "not an image of the true pattern [paradigma], but the true pattern itself. . . . Thus finally the harmony itself becomes entirely soul, nay even God." [23]

This, then, is the final justification of Kepler's search for mathematical harmonies. The investigation of nature becomes an investigation into the thought of God, Whom we can apprehend through the language of mathematics. *Mundus est imago Dei corporea,* just as, on the other hand, *animus est imago Dei incorporea.* In the end, Kepler's unifying principle for the world of phenomena is not merely the concept of mechanical forces, but God, expressing Himself in mathematical laws.

KEPLER'S TWO DEITIES

A final brief word may be in order concerning the psychological orientation of Kepler. Science, it must be remembered, was not Kepler's original destination. He was first a student of philosophy

---

[23] For a discussion of Kepler's mathematical epistemology and its relation to neo-Platonism, see Max Steck, "Über das Wesen des Mathematischen und die mathematische Erkenntnis bei Kepler," in *Die Gestalt* (Niemeyer, Halle, 1941), Vol. 5; the useful material is partly buried under nationalistic oratory. Another interesting source is A. Speiser, *Mathematische Denkweise* (Birkhäuser, Basel, 1945).

and theology at the University of Tübingen; only a few months before reaching the goal of a church position, he suddenly—and reluctantly—found himself transferred by the University authorities to a teaching position in mathematics and astronomy at Graz. A year later, while already working on the *Mysterium Cosmographicum,* Kepler wrote: "I wanted to become a theologian; for a long time I was restless: Now, however, observe how through my effort God is being celebrated in astronomy." [24] And more than a few times in his later writings he referred to astronomers as priests of the Deity in the book of nature.

From his earliest writings to his last, Kepler maintained the direction and intensity of his religio-philosophical interest. His whole life was one of uncompromising piety; he was incessantly struggling to uphold his strong and often nonconformist convictions in religion as in science. Caught in the turmoil of the counter-reformation and the beginning of the Thirty Years' War, in the face of bitter difficulties and hardships, he never compromised on issues of belief. Expelled from communion in the Lutheran Church for his unyielding individualism in religious matters, expelled from home and position at Graz for refusing to embrace Roman Catholicism, he could truly be believed when he wrote, "I take religion seriously, I do not play with it," [25] or "In all science there is nothing which could prevent me from holding an opinion, nothing which could deter me from acknowledging openly an opinion of mine, except solely the authority of the Holy Bible, which is being twisted badly by many." [26]

[24] Letter to Mästlin, October 3, 1595.
[25] Letter to Herwart, December 16, 1598.
[26] Letter to Herwart, March 28, 1605. If one wonders how Kepler resolved the topical conflict concerning the authority of the scriptures *versus* the authority of scientific results, the same letter contains the answer: "I hold that we must look into the intentions of the men who were inspired by the Divine Spirit. Except in the first chapter of Genesis concerning the supernatural origin of all things, they never intended to inform men concerning natural things." This view, later associated with Galileo, is further developed in Kepler's eloquent introduction to the *Astronomia Nova.* The relevant excerpts were first translated by Thomas Salusbury, *Mathematical Collections* (London, 1661), Part I, pp. 461-467.

But as his work shows us again and again, Kepler's soul bears a dual image on this subject too. For next to the Lutheran God, revealed to him directly in the words of the Bible, there stands the Pythagorean God, embodied in the immediacy of observable nature and in the mathematical harmonies of the solar system whose design Kepler himself had traced—a God "whom in the contemplation of the universe I can grasp, as it were, with my very hands." [27]

The expression is wonderfully apt: so intense was Kepler's vision that the abstract and concrete merged. Here we find the key to the enigma of Kepler, the explanation for the apparent complexity and disorder in his writings and commitments. In one brilliant image, Kepler saw the three basic cosmological models superposed: *the universe as physical machine, the universe as mathematical harmony, and the universe as central theological order*. And this was the setting in which harmonies were interchangeable with forces— in which a theocentric conception of the universe led to specific results of crucial importance for the rise of modern physics.

[27] Letter to Baron Strahlendorf, October 23, 1613.

# SELECTIVE BIBLIOGRAPHY

The following list consists principally of books by the authors of essays included in these two volumes. Most of the books contain extensive and up-to-date bibliographies.

Caspar, Max. *Johannes Kepler*. Translated by C. Doris Hellman. New York, Henry Schuman, 1960.

Castiglioni, Arturo. *History of Medicine*. rev. ed. New York, Alfred A. Knopf, 1947.

Crombie, A. C. *Medieval and Early Modern Science*. 2 vols. Garden City, New York, Doubleday Anchor Books, 1959. (Excellent bibliography.)

————. *Robert Grosseteste and the Origins of Experimental Science 1100-1700*. Oxford, Clarendon Press, 1953.

Dreyer, J. L. E. *History of the Planetary Systems from Thales to Kepler*. Cambridge, Cambridge University Press, 1906. Reprinted as *A History of Astronomy from Thales to Kepler,* New York, Dover Publications, 1953.

Duhem, Pierre. *Études sur Léonard de Vinci*. 3 vols. Paris, Hermann et Cie., 1906-1913.

————. *Le Système du monde. Histoire des doctrines cosmologiques de Platon à Copernic*. 10 vols. Paris, Hermann et Cie. Vols. I-V, 1913-1917; vols. VI-X, 1954-1959.

Holmyard, E. J. *Alchemy*. Baltimore, Penguin Books, 1957.

Morley, Henry. *Cornelius Agrippa*. 2 vols. London, Chapman & Hall, 1856.

——. *Jerome Cardan*. 2 vols. London, Chapman & Hall, 1854.

——. *Palissy the Potter*. 2 vols. 2nd ed. London, Chapman & Hall, 1855.

Pagel, Walter. *Paracelsus. An Introduction to Philosophical Medicine in the Era of the Renaissance*. Basel and New York, S. Karger, 1958.

Saunders, J. B. de C. M., and O'Malley, Charles D. (ed. and trans.) *The Illustrations from the Works of Andreas Vesalius of Brussels*. Cleveland and New York, World Publishing Co., 1950.

Sigerist, Henry E. *On the History of Medicine*. Edited by F. Martí-Ibáñez. MD Publications, 1960.

Singer, Charles, *et al.* (ed.) *A History of Technology*. Vols. I-V. Oxford and New York: Oxford University Press, 1954-1958.

——. *The Evolution of Anatomy*. London, Kegan Paul, Trench, Trubner & Co., 1925. Reprinted as *A Short History of Anatomy and Physiology*, New York, Dover Publications, 1959.

Taylor, F. Sherwood. *The Alchemists. Founders of Modern Chemistry*. New York, Henry Schuman, 1949.